JUN - 1977

NEWARK PUBLIC LIBRARY - NEWARK, OHIO 43055

3 2487 00046 2771

910.45

Armstrong.

Sea phantoms.

WITHDRAWN

W9-BXL-730

NEWARK PUBLIC LIBRARY
NEWARK, OHIO

SEA PHANTOMS

Sea Phantoms

N 32

WARREN ARMSTRONG

The John Day Company
New York

© *1961 BY WILLIAM E. BENNETT*

All rights reserved. This book, or parts thereof, must not be reproduced in any form without permission. Published by The John Day Company, 62 West 45th Street, New York 36, N. Y., and on the same day in Canada by Longmans, Green & Company, Toronto.

LIBRARY OF CONGRESS CATALOGUE CARD NUMBER: 61-7490

MANUFACTURED IN THE UNITED STATES OF AMERICA

Acknowledgment

My sincere thanks for their ready and kindly help in providing me with material for this book are due to the many people, from every part of the world, who wrote to me and whom I visited in the course of research. They are too numerous to list here, but I shall not easily forget them, nor the incidents which they related to me.

611587

Contents

Foreword

Dr. Samuel Johnson once observed: "All logic is against ghosts, but all experience is for them"; and Shakespeare had Hamlet say of them: "They come in such questionable shape."

Phantoms belong to a nightmare world; a world where intense anguish or mental torture, or cruelty, vengeance, murder and hate have contributed toward creating certain conditions which bind the spectral world to our own. These things drag a spirit back to human surroundings, ashore and, I submit, afloat, and not all ghosts belong to the darkest periods of the Middle Ages. Psychic experts have recently proved the existence of phantoms driving around in spectral automobiles. So why not spectral ships?

Like many another seafaring man, I am tempted to believe in phantoms, yet I am a down-to-earth individual and usually refuse to accept anything without adequate proof; nevertheless, much as I have tried, I cannot discover any rational explanation for incidents set down in this book. With any normal man, I deprecate the suggestion of the supernatural, but I fail in most instances to offer any alternative theory.

W. A.

SEA PHANTOMS

I

The Case of the Haunted
U-Boat

WHEN World War I erupted there were, in Washington and London, skeptics who regarded the submarine with a fair measure of disbelief bordering on contempt; a submarine, they claimed, could never hope to achieve measurable success in any all-out war at sea. German experts did not subscribe to that view and within months of the declaration of war even the most optimistic prophecies of Imperial Germany's navy chiefs were surpassed.

In the North Sea, to prove their point, U-boats sought out and in a matter of minutes destroyed three British cruisers, *Aboukir*, *Hogue* and *Cressy;* when the first successful torpedo attack was registered and the other two warships stopped to rescue survivors they were at once attacked and sunk. It was a spectacular feat, and it caused near panic in the minds of the British navy chiefs, who visualized immense losses among vital supply ships and defeat through sheer starvation. Orders were placed for more submarines than Britain had shipyards for building them, and the United States was approached for assistance. Without such aid it could have been a case of touch and go.

In Berlin, after two years of naval warfare, with increasing submarine successes, Admiral von Holtzendorff reported to the Kaiser: "Unrestricted U-boat attack against enemy merchant shipping bringing food and munitions from America to Britain and her Allies can force our enemies to their knees within six months."

At that period Germany had many skilled and determined submarine commanders and crews who may have lacked other virtues, but they did not lack courage. In the first months of the war U-boats had observed international rules and demonstrated their captains' skill and efficiency; but as war progressed German navy chiefs ordered that a policy of sink on sight, regardless of human suffering, must be carried out. It was war to the knife edge, and when it reaches that stage it is usually the innocent who pay the extreme price.

Admiral von Capelle, Secretary of the Imperial German Navy from March, 1916, to September, 1918, was charged with personal responsibility to build and increase the U-boat fleet, the greater part of which was scheduled to operate around the northern and southern approaches to the Irish Sea and the western approaches to the English Channel. To Admiral Schroeder, von Capelle delegated personal responsibility for

14

fast and increased submarine construction in the captured shipyards of Bruges.

So, in the early summer of 1916, unrestricted jubilation was apparent among officers and crews of the Flanders U-boat flotilla, for the Imperial Navy's undersea offensive was nearing peak and enemy merchant shipping was being destroyed at such a rate that it could be only a matter of months before the enemy was forced to sue for peace. The Flanders flotilla had been chiefly responsible for this success, and the awarding of Iron Crosses was liberal; surely, then, this was time to celebrate. . . .

In the early fall of 1916, Admiral Schroeder came into Bruges, his visit a dual-purpose one; another batch of Iron Crosses were to be awarded on the Kaiser's personal orders and, afterward, the mass launch of another submarine flotilla. Schroeder made his way to a wine cellar adequately proofed against enemy air attack, and surveyed the general scene. Though the food shortage at home was at its worst, here in Bruges U-boat personnel lived off the fat of the land.

Here, indeed, was no shortage of rich, rare foods, and expensive local wines flowed freely; flaxen-haired girls who had followed the all-conquering Imperial flag across the Rhine were busy making life reasonably pleasant for young submarine officers on shore leave. Schroeder had no time for this kind of thing. His primary task was to whip the enemy. But once in a while he was willing to turn a blind eye on the pleasures of men who spent a large part of their service careers in the gray-green depth of the seas. Tonight meant little to a man like Schroeder. It was tomorrow that really mattered.

In the morning, shortly after the first light of dawn, from the nearby U-boat pens would emerge the nation's greatest effort thus far to end this war, to put the final turn of the thumbscrew on an enemy whose empty stomachs were already demanding peace. England was verging on collapse mainly because the Flanders U-boat flotilla had sunk supply ships faster than they could be built. And tomorrow, from Bruges, would go twenty-four new submarines for operational duties all around the coasts of Britain. Schroeder accepted a glass of wine, sipped it, and retired for the night.

The twenty-four new craft were of the same class, measuring around 510 tons, with a cruising speed of 15 knots, manned by three officers and thirty-one enlisted men, with a sprinkling of seasoned U-boat veterans to add moral support to new men. With one strange exception, there was nothing to differentiate the vessels of the new flotilla; that one exception was *UB-65* which had assumed all the peculiarities of a ship to make her "hoodoo."

During the initial stages of her building a heavy girder had slipped from slings, crashed on the slipway, killing one man outright and injuring a second so severely that he died in agony before reaching the base hospital. That would have been bad enough—an ill omen among superstitious shipyard workers; but some weeks later, the U-boat nearly completed, her engine room had become choked with fumes and three more men died.

German Navy Security clamped down tight on these incidents, mainly for reasons of morale, and that was understandable. In early dawn light, Admiral Schroeder carried out a simple launching ceremony; the *UB-65* and her sister ships slipped moorings and shortly before noon got under way, heading out for trials in the North Sea. From that moment chapters were to be written of the most terrifying and authentic ghost story of the seven seas.

There is always a certain act of finality in the closing of the last hatch in any submarine. Among commanders of any underwater vessel of any nation it was always a pretty tough man who did not pause just an instant as he put on the last clips and locked them with their pins . . . and wondered, for a split second, what he and his crew might experience before they again breathed pure fresh air. Weather conditions were only moderately good when the new flotilla left harbor for the exercise area, but by mid-afternoon off the small island of Noordland, at the entrance to the Ooster Schelde, a freshening wind piled up the seas and threatened a rough passage.

Preparatory to taking the ship into her first dive, the *UB-65*'s commander ordered an experienced member of the crew to make an inspection of the forward part of the hull; that man climbed out of the conning tower *and deliberately walked overboard*. It was all over with startling suddenness; one moment he was there, the next, gone. Certainly, he had not lost foothold, nor were the seas rough enough to pitch him overboard. With some members of the crew superstitious enough to place their own construction on yet another death, the commander determined to maintain strict discipline. He locked the last hatch clips securely, ordered a thorough check of all valves and compartments, took a last look around, jabbed a thumb hard against the button of the diving hooter. Then, as the submarine gathered speed and depth, he called "Thirty feet!" and a white feather of foam and spray marked the *UB-65*'s descent.

For the next dozen hours the submarine lay immovable on the sea bed, failing to respond to every effort to take her up. Water entered her hull, reached the batteries, and the air became poisoned by evil fumes. When at last she surfaced and the conning tower could be opened and fresh air let in, officers and men were more dead than alive.

When she returned to Bruges and was taken alongside to load supplies—ammunition and torpedoes for her first operational tour of duty—a warhead exploded. When the smoke had cleared, the *UB-65*'s second lieutenant and five enlisted men lay sprawled in death, with several others severely injured. At once a formal report was sent to Admiral Schroeder and the submarine was ordered into dry dock for extensive repairs, her crew taking shore leave in watches while work was in progress. And then it happened.

A petty officer of the watch stumbled panic-stricken into the wardroom and collapsed at the feet of an astonished first lieutenant; revived, the fear-crazed man stumbled into a corner of the small compartment, covered his eyes with trembling hands, and cried: "The dead man's come aboard!" He was accused of being drunk on duty and ordered to his quarters, but he pleaded: "Not me alone, Herr Oberleutnant, Pedersen saw the Thing, too!"

With his junior officer, the first lieutenant went on deck, where Pedersen was discovered crouched in terror by the conning tower, stammering, "God help us all! We both saw him come aboard and walk slowly to the bows; and there he stood, arms folded across his breast, staring at us."

"Who? Who was it you are supposed to have seen?" demanded the first lieutenant.

"The second officer . . . the man who was killed when that warhead exploded."

Both men were brought before the *UB-65*'s commander. He listened to what they had to tell him, then dismissed them. He called the other officers into the wardroom. "You will say nothing whatever," he told them, "in any place or to anybody, of this regrettable incident, you understand? If you disobey this order I shall place you under close arrest. It is my belief that somebody has perpetrated a practical joke. Either that or it could be the work of British secret agents seeking to harm the morale of our submarine crews. If that is the game, we shall see!"

Two days later, an hour before the submarine left for her first operational tour of duty, Pedersen deserted and was never heard of again. Among his personal effects he left a note addressed to the commander warning that the U-boat and all who served in her were doomed.

"Hoodoo" or not, the *UB-65* left base, shaped a westerly course, negotiated the Dover Straits barrage, sighted an Allied supply ship off the coast of Kent, torpedoed it and sheered off in safety. The following day she surfaced some fifteen miles off the British naval base of Portland, Dorset, and orders were given for batteries to be charged. Lookouts were posted to port and starboard of her conning tower and, as a spiteful wind blew sheets of salt water into their faces, did their best to maintain constant watch.

An hour passed. Then, shaking with fear, his face drawn in terror, the starboard lookout cried for the officer of the watch. Pointing to the bows of the ship, he screamed, "It's there! Look. . . . Its arms folded like Pedersen said it stood, silent, not moving through the seas sweep across the ship. It's not one of us. It's the dead second officer!" Then he fainted.

Cupping his hands, the first lieutenant called, "You, there!" The vague figure turned about and stared toward the conning tower, revealing in the fading light the features of the dead officer whose broken body lay buried in the naval cemetery at Wilhelmshavn. The first lieutenant summoned the commander and, together, the two men stared unbelieving at the apparition. When at last it disappeared the *UB-65* dived deep, as if her commander wished to put as much distance between them and the phantom as possible. But he was aware that his crew went gloomily about their duties, filled with unspoken fears. Men on watch glanced quickly over their shoulders or huddled in a compartment, never muttering a word among them.

A spell of action did little to change the mood of the crew as, in the course of the next three days the *UB-65* overtook and torpedoed a sizable supply ship heading for Plymouth, crippled a second by gunfire but left the victim awash and afloat, listing badly. The commander refused to sink the ship. He feared it might be destined to bring total destruction to the submarine if they sought to sink their quarry; they would leave her to the mercy of the seas and any enemy vessel that might happen along. Meantime, the *UB-65* made for base, where her commander stepped ashore to enter his report. Just as his feet touched dry land, either a German anti-aircraft shell splinter, or part of a bomb from Allied aircraft raiding the base, sheered off his head. Moments later an enlisted man stumbled ashore crying that the dead second lieutenant had appeared again to take up the same position on the U-boat's bows.

Schroeder was handed a confidential report on the succession of strange incidents and, with the commodore of submarines, went aboard the *UB-65* and cross-examined every member of the crew. The interrogation completed, he ordered the men on leave and the submarine to be taken into a dockyard pen. And there she was left, silent, deserted. The following day she was visited by a Lutheran chaplain who conducted a service to exorcise evil spirits.

A new commander was appointed, a tough, well-tried veteran of the service; a man who let it be known form the start that he would tolerate "no damned nonsense," and that any man who so much as breathed the word "ghost" would languish in the brig on bread and water.

The *UB-65* left on her next operational tour, succeeded in destroying much tonnage of Allied merchant ships and returned to Bruges without incident. Command was given to Oberleutnant Schelle, another seasoned submarine commander, whom Admiral Schroeder always admired for his courage and discipline. At this time, however, a chief petty officer of the *UB-65* wrote a letter:

> We were never a pack of nervous fools, and we have known from the first day we served in the ship that there was something evil about her. Not one of us ever put name to it, nor understood these frightening experiences, but we never thought we saw the ghost; we never imagined anything. What we saw, we saw, and that is all. I am among many members of our present crew who have seen the wraith of our dead second officer, standing always in the bows, with his arms folded. One night, lying sleepless in my bunk, I watched terrified as the phantom entered my quarters and then walked past me and disappeared into our forward torpedo room. It never came out again. He never knew it, but on many occasions I saw our previous

commander, the man who threatened us with punishment if we so much as mentioned the word 'ghost,' look over his shoulder and tremble. It was not until he handed over command to Schelle that I heard from his steward that he declared the ship to be haunted. I am due to sail in the *UB-65* for her next tour of duty, but I pray that I may be stricken by some severe illness, or wounded in action and taken into a hospital, so that I may live to tell my story one day.

In May, 1918, the *UB-65* slipped her moorings and left base with three other units of the flotilla. Their orders were to proceed along the English Channel, make for the Bay of Biscay and there intercept and destroy an important Allied convoy.

Off Finisterre, the *UB-65*'s leading gunner, named Eberhardt, went berserk, screaming that he had brushed shoulders with the ghost of the dead second lieutenant. After a scuffle he was restrained, given an injection of morphine and left under guard. Reviving, he found his chance and committed suicide. That night the U-boat's engineer lieutenant broke a leg and developed a high fever. Then, shortly after dawn when the U-boats surfaced for a spell before proceeding in search of the convoy, Petty Officer Richard Meyer rushed to the conning tower, climbed out, jumped into the sea and deliberately swam out of sight. When night fell, the Allied convoy was sighted and the U-boats closed in, but an unexpected depth-charge attack sent the *UB-65* hurtling to the sea bed.

A member of the crew, describing subsequent events

many months after the war, told how the world of gray-green around the submarine seemed to "go mad" as the dim glow of electric lamps wavered and faded out. The current breaker came adrift under the impact of explosion from depth charges, and injured men lay gasping for life in half-flooded compartments with a strange, whitish-green light seeming to creep around their bodies. Then, somewhere in that frightening half light a seaman laughed crazily: *"Herr Gott!* It's here— here at my side! I can feel its cold fingers touching my cheek!"

The *UB-65*'s commander shouted an order and a junior officer drew his Luger pistol and fired in the direction of the demented seaman; then another explosion sent the submarine reeling drunkenly. Yet, by miraculous navigation, the crippled ship limped back to base, where her commander reported to Schroeder that he had seen the ghost of the dead second officer on two occasions. He was at once relieved of his ship. The entire crew was replaced while the submarine dry-docked for refitting.

On the morning of July 10, 1918, off Cape Clear, the United States submarine *L-2*, on patrol at periscope depth, sighted a suspicious object on the horizon and closed to investigate. Her captain made it out for what it was . . . the *UB-65*, surfaced, apparently unmanned and derelict. He edged *L-2* into position to attack and her torpedoes were made ready; they were never to be fired. Moments later a violent explosion blotted out the U-boat, though not before the *L-2*'s captain had made out through his periscope the figure of a man, arms folded across his breast, standing motionless on the U-boat's bows.

German Naval Headquarters on July 31, 1918, admitted in a communiqué: "One of our submarines, the *UB-65*, is missing and must be presumed lost with thirty-four officers and men." That was all—merely the terse official announcement. And when they read it, veterans of the Flanders flotilla said it was to be expected, anyway; the *UB-65* "always carried an extra officer whose ghostly hand piloted the ship to her predestined doom!"

Professor Hecht, well-known German psychologist, who investigated the case of the *UB-65* and who later published an official summary of his findings, details of which were never made public, wrote: "This phenomenon does not lend itself to any explanation. I can put forward no alternative theory to the supernatural agency which finally brought about the destruction of this ill-fated vessel."

Was it a phantom that took the *UB-65* to her doom? Could it have been a case of mass hallucination? And was that final, fearful explosion caused by some obstruction at the end of a torpedo tube which detonated other torpedoes ready for firing? Nobody will ever know; nor, for that matter, will anybody who knew or served in the *UB-65* confirm or dispute the presence of that silent figure that stood motionless on the ship's bows.

2.

The Burning Ghost Ship of Block Island

THEY were spacious days, those old Colonial times, when a handful of hard-working folk set about the task of building a new world, bounded on the east by three thousand miles of ocean, on the west by un-explored, unknown territory. They were also days of austerity.

The ground they had selected for their first settle-ments was thin, the soil stony, and somehow they would have to wring a living from it. It would mean felling tall timber, using it to build houses, workshops, and ships, too, because the sea must provide them with food.

They had traveled this far and there was no turning back. This was life, not the living hell they had known back in Europe. This was opportunity. Opportunity that came with labor, trail-blazing, courage, endurance, but offered peace and freedom.

The majority had inherited bold seafaring tradition, and that first year, 1631, after the great Puritan migra-

DW   I LOVE MWR

tion to New England began, shipwrights were busy on the Mystic River constructing one of the New World's first deep-sea vessels, *Blessing of the Bay*, a stout, sixty-ton sloop owned by Governor John Winthrop. Twelve years later, one of those pioneers wrote: "Besides many boats, shallops, pinnaces and lighters, we are in a way of building ships of one hundred, two hundred, three hundred and even four hundred tons, and five such ships are already at sea with many more in hand." In fact, in 1641, Salem shipwrights launched their first deep-sea ship, twice the size of the *Mayflower*, under the guidance of Hugh Peters, pastor of the First Church. From Newburyport south to New Haven, the sound of adze and hammer created a new anthem of faith among men whose veins held the salt of the sea.

It was in 1647 that a chronicler wrote:

We had suffered hereabouts in New Haven a series of depressing reverses in trade and industry, so we sought to retrieve ourselves by building a 150-ton ship to freight her for England. Our fine vessel sailed away manned by the best and bravest of our town, but one slow month followed another and we had no tidings of its arrival overseas. We were sadly distraught until, one day, after a great thunder storm about one hour before sunset, a ship of exactly like dimensions, with her canvas and colors set, appeared in the air coming up the harbor against the wind for the space of one hour. Among us was the Rev. Mr. Pierpont who had been called to behold this great work of the Lord; yea, our very children cried out *"There* is a brave ship!" When so near that any one of our number might easily hurl a stone on board, the vessel's main top seemed blown off,

27

then her mizzentop, then her masting was blown away; before our wondering eyes she overset and so vanished completely into a smoky cloud. The vision was given, we knew, that we might now understand the tragic end of our first deep-sea ship and of our friends in her.

Not every member of the community of New Haven could have been psychic; nor could the majority have possessed second sight and the ability to see things which others could not. Yet those men, women and children of New Haven claimed to have witnessed the strange apparition. Research workers, well-versed in psychic matters, maintain that phantoms are concomitants of remorse, strong feelings of possession, shock, violent death, intense anguish, cruelty in some terrible form, vengeance, black thoughts, blacker deeds. Which of these conjured this ghost ship? Shock, intense anguish, violent death—who can possibly know?

Little more than a century later, in 1752, there sailed from Holland an emigrant ship provided from the start with every element for supernatural doom—cruelty and hate, mental torture, human suffering; here, too, was the unquenchable urge for vengeance.

The story of the ship *Palatine* is typical of the period, mid-1700 to mid-1800, when the traffic of emigrants from Europe bound for eastern Atlantic ports reached flood proportions, at that time when the North Atlantic crossing drew its patrons from two classes: those impelled by the promise of trade, and those driven by despair to seek their fortunes in the New World. Of the two, the latter were overwhelmingly the more numerous, eager to give everything they owned to make the voyage.

The *Palatine* was a typical emigrant vessel, around the eight-hundred-ton mark, rather less than 200 feet in length, less than 40 feet at her widest. Of the living space available, there was the fo'c'sle, where the crew lived on hard tack and a twice-weekly ration of meat, potatoes, pickles, molasses and bread; the cabin and staterooms aft, where captain and passengers lived in a style not too far removed from life ashore; and the remaining two thirds of the vessel, in a rectangular compartment some hundred feet long and 30 feet wide, where hundreds of emigrants tried, often unsuccessfully, to live on what food they brought with them.

Of normal personal or domestic amenities the *Palatine* provided none; not even a stool was available. If a passenger wished to sit he had either to squat on his haunches on the evil-smelling deck of the barnlike compartment, or on the shapeless bundle containing his worldly possessions. Bereft of the vaguest trace of privacy, the poor emigrants were crowded together to survive the arduous voyage as best they could or die in the attempt.

Four hundred and thirteen passengers had boarded this floating hovel the previous voyage, and turned their eyes west hopefully. The 3,000-mile crossing had taken ninety-seven days, and seventeen emigrants had starved to death; the remainder stumbled ashore more dead than alive. On this present voyage three hundred and four emigrants embarked and only a few were to live. The crossing lasted eighty-four days. From available records, the story of the last voyage of the *Palatine* is reconstructed—the story of a ship destined to become a phantom. . . .

Any person with a fair notion of what a full-rigged ocean-going schooner ought to look like would never have claimed the *Palatine* came anywhere near specifications. Seamen passing her moored at the water front held their breath, swearing they could smell the worms in her. She was just a rank bad ship, a shade worse than most others making the shuttle service between European and eastern Atlantic seaboard ports; but to emigrants she was a vital link in the great escape route to freedom. Nothing else mattered—at least not until the voyage started, and then they learned how bad a ship could be.

Among the schooner's severest critics was a likable little Amsterdam shipwright whose craft had been handed down to him through five generations. His father had helped build the *Palatine* and watched her come down her slipway and head out to sea, trading around the Levant, carrying Dutch, French and Spanish products from port to port. At that time the schooner had flown her national flag proudly, as if to tell the world that Holland was supreme at sea. In those days, too, her captain, officers and crew had behaved like good sailormen.

But with the passing years, and with trade developing, business was too brisk to allow time for periodic overhaul, and she began to show unmistakable signs of wear and neglect. Slowly she deteriorated, and so did the men who worked her. Her captain believed that a ship could be handled better with belaying pin, knuckle-duster and whisky than with sextant, charts and compass. Soon, decent seamen gave the ship and her captain a wide berth. Her crew were dredged from waterfront sweepings or shanghaied from boardinghouses operated by crimps—a drunken, rascally crowd. Killers. Like their captain.

Amsterdam sparkled in the warm sunlight as the *Palatine*'s first emigrant passengers reached the water front and there stood a while in silence looking back on this place that had been home. Here were the well-known bridges connecting the small islands that made up the city; and the Guild House, which Rembrandt had used as background for his painting *The Anatomy Lesson*; and the Oude Kerke, behind the Warmoes-straat, the Nieuwe Kerke, close by the palace on the Dam. Here was silent glory. Here was home.

Now they were leaving all this behind, for Holland could no longer support its growing population; work was becoming scarce and the soil was too poverty-stricken to grow sufficient food.

The little Dutch shipwright, with his crippled wife and infant daughter, had reached his decision, sold their home and few possessions, and with nothing left but the tools of his trade, was ready to sail into the west. There he would find work, helping to build ships— work that would provide a new home, peace and prosperity, and freedom to live the life they wanted, to worship as they wished. Their baby daughter would grow to womanhood and one day marry and bear children who would become Americans. . . .

So they reached the water front and stood with scores of fellow emigrants looking over the ships. The little Dutchman's eyes traveled across the lines of the *Palatine* and the sight distressed him. To him, a ship was like a woman, needing care and affection; for if a man used a woman or a ship badly he could hurt them and they would become sullen, likely as not display ill-temper or nerves. A man who treated either in such a manner would break the heart of a woman or lose his ship. The little Dutchman sniffed in disgust. A man who neglected his ship was no seaman.

He picked up a carpetbag containing his tools, lifted their child in his free arm and made his way aboard the schooner, leaving both on deck while he returned for his wife. It was hard for a woman to be rendered helpless, to depend upon her man for nearly every need. He could never forget the night their child was born, when something had gone wrong and left his wife stricken, with one side paralyzed.

He lifted her in his arms and carried her aboard the schooner, where he collided with the *Palatine*'s bucko mate who struck out at him, bringing a thin smear of blood from his lips. The little Dutchman swallowed hard and his eyes blazed; then he carried his wife below deck and settled her and the child in a dark corner of the barnlike compartment. He looked around and reckoned there would be no more than eighteen inches or so of space between the tiers of wooden bunks covered by stinking straw where hundreds of men, women and children would try to sleep throughout the long voyage.

Smoking horn lanterns swinging in gimbals flickered a mockery of light around this rectangular box, already stale with fetid air. He comforted his wife and child, telling them not to despair. Above their heads the heavy boots of seamen punctuated the cries of a child somewhere in the semidarkness. . . .

An hour before flood tide the *Palatine*'s captain stumped aboard, strode to his room, slammed the door, and half-emptied a bottle. An evil mood filled him. He drained the rest of the bottle, pitched it into fragments against a bulkhead, and stumbled to his berth.

For five years, since 1747, he had helped carry these whining emigrants across the North Atlantic, and with them a sizable tonnage in freight. Emigrants and freight represented profit—not for him but for his employers. There was little enough to show for his labors except what money he had managed to extract through the crimps and, every so often when an emigrant died at sea, his privileged first pickings among their personal possessions.

The *Palatine* always made landfall off Block Island, on Long Island Sound. Block Island had a sinister reputation, the home of wreckers who for years had successfully lured emigrant ships to their doom by showing false lights. Plenty of vessels had landed there, the passengers stripped of possessions as they struggled ashore;

and any foolish emigrants who had shown fight were flung back into the sea. Dead men cannot tell tales. . . . As far as the schooner's captain was concerned, it was a matter of no importance whether his emigrant passengers lived or died.

At the conclusion of the previous voyage he had talked over his plan with the wreckers. The *Palatine* would be deliberately driven ashore, plundered, and all profits from the sale of looted freight and from the passengers' belongings, or from the bodies of those who died, would be shared with the captain.

The weather held good, a light following wind billowed the schooner's canvas and sent her on her way westward at a steady clip. It was as if the *Palatine* was demonstrating her ability to earn profits for many a North Atlantic voyage yet to come—as if her days were not numbered.

Then came a break-up in the weather. Sea and wind combined their weight and smashed at the ship with sledge-hammer ferocity. The welter of this elemental sound stifled the cries of panic-stricken women and children below deck. On the nineteenth day out, the *Palatine*'s first mate pounded into the emigrant quarters, lined up every man, woman and child and systematically searched them for personal possessions. When a man resisted he was ruthlessly knocked down and his body shoved into a dark corner; so far as the mate was concerned, it could rot there. During the following ten days, with the schooner laboring against continued heavy weather, nine babies were born . . . and nine

34

babies died; so, too, did five of the young mothers. Cholera broke out in the emigrant quarters.

Eighty-two nightmare days and nights the terror continued. Supplies of food neared the vanishing point, and drinking water was rationed to one tin mugful for each passenger, although they knew that in his stateroom quarters, the *Palatine*'s captain and a dozen wealthy passengers fared well on meat and wine. Such a state of affairs created despair, mental torture, hate and the urge for revenge.

On the morning of the eighty-third day, the little Dutchman comforted his crippled wife, snugged their child into her arms, stumbled wearily toward the bolted hatch cover. He pried it open, crawled out, and was at once smitten by a monstrous wind that hurt his lungs. He got to his feet shakily and took stock of his whereabouts. He wanted to find the room where an inhuman beast called the captain spent his time in half-drunken stupor. The little Dutchman wanted to kill, to avenge the bestial deeds inflicted upon them all from the day of the schooner's departure.

He dodged the stinging spume of an onrushing sea, regained his balance, braced his body against the next drenching onslaught, then stood unbelieving as his eyes caught sight of a wide-winged fulmar circling the ship, screaming for food. He stared at this graceful bird, now close enough for him to see its bright, beadlike eyes; presently it disappeared on the veering wind. And he knew that land was near. He dropped to his knees, muttered a prayer of gratitude that the voyage was soon end-ing; he stumbled back to his wife, took her in his arms and told her the news. From one to another, word of their deliverance was passed. In a turmoil of suppressed excitement emigrants bundled together what was left of their treasures and made ready to step ashore on dry land. They gathered below the barred hatch covers, awaiting sight of the sky above. . . .

Guided by the false beacon of the wreckers, the *Palatine* ran aground on the southeastern extremity of Block Island and shuddered to rest. Minutes passed before the emigrants realized what had happened; then a huge sea rushed at the schooner, pouring its weight over her starboard quarter, forcing the ship down to an alarming angle. The main deckhouse was torn away and swept overboard. Released from the hellhole that had been their living quarters for so many long weeks, emigrants poured out on the deck. Those who sought safety in the rigging were torn clear and pitched into the sea as a vast comber climbed into the rigging and receded. Yard by yard, the *Palatine* was lifted with each incoming sea and shifted ashore. And then came the wreckers. . . .

Every scheme devised by the *Palatine*'s captain went by the board as ghouls climbed aboard, broke open hatchways, hauled freight on deck and lowered it into longboats. Next they turned their attention to the emigrants, dragged them from hiding places, ill-treated and stripped them, flung them into the sea. Other victims, terror-stricken, climbed the ship's rail and dropped into the swirling waters, striking out for land. Few of these survived.

The little Dutchman struggled to carry his wife to the safety of the deck, treading with infinite care lest she lose hold of their child. His aim was to reach the rail and, with his precious burden, drop overboard in the hope of being carried ashore. He stumbled across the body of an emigrant and fell headlong. When he recovered his senses he knew he was alone. His wife and child were gone. One arm hung loose, broken. Easing himself across the sloping deck, he fell into the breakers and was carried ashore. There he sought his loved ones.

Dawn had broken when he had stumbled to shore. For hours he searched for his wife and child. He was nearing collapse; and then, as daylight faded, out of a gray sky he saw the first tongue of red flame. Bewildered, he hardly dared to accept what his eyes told him. The *Palatine* was on fire. He could hear the timbers cracking open with a sound like cannon fire.

Looted of everything of value, stripped down to a skeleton, the schooner had been fired by the wreckers so that evidence of their crime would never be discovered. So she blazed all that day and through the night to the next watery dawn . . . and in that inferno of flame and heat a woman still sought her child. Dragging her stricken body she crawled among the embers. A broken mast fell and crushed an arm, and a smoke-blackened sheaf block struck her temple and gashed it. She cried the name of her child; and she knew she was alone, deserted.

From the shore, terrified emigrants watched the passing of the ship, and screamed in horror when they made out the figure of a woman clinging to the last unburnt part of the deckhouse. Agonizing moments later she vanished from sight as the last hungry flame licked around the timber where she had been seen. By morning all traces of the *Palatine* had disappeared; but ashore in their dwellings, the Block Island wreckers wished that the sight of that demented woman were blotted from memory.

Twelve months later to the day, the grim shape of the *Palatine* reappeared off Block Island and was seen by scores of people; in later years the phantom was seen, so they claimed, by men like Captain John Collins, master of the North Atlantic packet *Roscius*, of the Dramatic Line; by Captain Asa Eldridge, master of the *Pacific*; Captain Samuels, of the North Atlantic pacemaker *Dreadnought*, and by captain and crew of the New Bedford whaler *Montreal*, homeward bound from the Arctic waters.

Were men like these, along with scores of shore folk, laboring under some delusion? It seems hard to accept. Disbelieving people who heard the legend dismissed it with fine cynicism. When it was probed in the mid-1800's, evidence was produced that a Block Island woman originated the story. What was surely interesting, but never investigated, was her claim to be the child of the little Dutch shipwright and his paralyzed wife. Was that a mere figment of imagination? Nobody put forward evidence to the contrary.

Maybe the phantom shape of the ghost ship off Block Island was no more than phosphorescence—St. Elmo's fire is a perfectly natural phenomenon, an electrical manifestation due to the atmospheric state immediately before or during a severe storm.

On numerous occasions the "fire" has been seen as a light closely resembling flame, playing around a ship's rigging and masts. It was known back in ancient Grecian times. Greek seafarers centuries later knew it as "corpo santo." And William Dampier recorded: "Towards late in the day thunder and rain abated, and then we clearly saw a Corpus Sant at our mainmast head on the very top of the truck. The sight rejoiced our crew exceedingly, for the worst of any storm is commonly believed over when the Corpus Sant is seen aloft, but when it can be seen clearly from the deck it is accounted an evil omen, a bad sign."

A bishop of old Sicily, St. Elmo was stricken by fatal illness while on voyage, and is said to have told captain and crew that if he died he would appear to them and save the ship from disaster. Immediately after his death a light did in fact appear at the masthead, and was so named after him.

But there is another, maybe more acceptable, explanation; that worthy authority on seafaring matters, Captain John Smith, in his *Seaman's Grammar*, a treatise published in 1627, quoted the case of a ship's lookout who reported to his captain that a ship of the line, the old-time equivalent of a modern warship, was approaching over the horizon. When the two vessels neared each other, the "ship of the line" was proved to be a small brig; what had happened was that, when first sighted at extreme distance, she had "loomed"; she had, in fact, assumed the indistinct proportions of a warship—an exaggerated appearance due to an optical phenomenon, possibly refraction.

Similarly, the beam from most lighthouses can be *seen* from, say, a distance of fifteen miles, but the beam's *loom* is often clearly sighted in fine weather as far distant as fifty to seventy miles; again, an optical illusion. Also, immediately before bad weather, or with extremely good visibility around most coastlines, distant objects are often projected and magnified.

In the final analysis, it appears to be impossible not to associate the legend of the ill-fated *Palatine* with St. Elmo's fire; and the account, referred to in authoritative histories of the American Merchant Marine, of the "return" to New Haven of a lost freighter with the phenomenon of mirage, by which a vessel below the horizon can sometimes be seen plainly *in the air above it*. Sea mirage has been responsible for a number of remarkable sights. In 1854, in the Baltic, when a British naval squadron of nineteen vessels was more than thirty miles distant, it was sighted floating in the upper air, magnified out of all proportion against a background haze of colored mist.

Who can say whether the burning phantom of the *Palatine* did not return to the scene of her Block Island wreck; or that the good people of New Haven did not witness that strange apparition? At least, Pastor Pierpont was prepared to make a sworn affidavit that he saw it, and it would seem to be ungenerous to doubt the word of a man of his caliber.

3.

Fratricide, Falkenberg and the FD-12

A SNOW SQUALL blotted out visibility when our forward gunner reported he could hear a whistling sound that certainly did not originate in the flotilla of light naval forces patrolling the 500-mile area off the Norwegian coast. Somewhere overhead in that freezing opaqueness an aircraft was circling, trying, maybe, to find a hole in the ceiling and take a look at what was happening.

Thirty minutes later we picked him out of the North Sea, more dead than alive, a regulation football referee's whistle frozen tight in his lips. We brought him aboard, snugged him down, waited until he could tell us his story. When he did, he said the whistle had been his lucky charm during fifteen years as first officer on a freighter plying between Norwegian and United Kingdom east-coast ports. It was the only thing he had left, besides his clothing, after an enemy bomber scored a bull's-eye amidships. He was the sole survivor.

We landed him safely at a British base, but not before half a dozen of us had listened to the story he had to tell. He said, "So there it is. I'm no more superstitious than the average seafaring man, but I swear I saw the Falkenberg ship the night we sailed out of Lysekil." He raised his glass of brandy and said "Skoal!" We nodded "Skoal!" and wished him well in whatever job he would be given after the Allied interrogation people had satisfied themselves he was not a Nazi agent. His story rang true enough, up to the point where he introduced this Falkenberg character and claimed that spectral visitations giving warning of impending disaster had their counterparts at sea as well as on land. In that flotilla operating in the North Sea during the years 1941 to 1943, we reckoned we had quite enough on our hands worrying about the human element pitted against us night and day, seven days a week, without concerning ourselves about ghosts.

Looking back on that incident after a lapse of seventeen years, anybody but the most critical skeptic might be tempted to connect three or four strange events with a six-hundred-year-old legend accepted as true by seamen of half a dozen European countries serving in ships around the North Sea.

First, though, around the turn of this century a poet named W. W. Gibson set down the makings of a grim story about the crew of a Scottish lighthouse—a strange story that never made headline news.

On the night of December 15, 1900, homeward bound for the Port of Greenock, on the west coast of

Scotland, a small freighter skirting the Isle of Lewis on a southwesterly course failed to pick up the warning light from Flannan Island. This was one of the loneliest beacons in Europe, mounting guard over a group of isles, a dreaded danger area about fifteen miles off the Hebrides. Reaching port, the freighter's captain reported that the light was not showing, but for reasons never made known, the Scottish Lighthouse Board was not notified.

Eleven days later, December 26, the Board's supply ship *Hesperus* sailed from her base in command of Captain Harvey, headed for Flannan Island to put relief keeper Joseph Moore ashore and take home the man he was relieving.

On the island were three men: chief keeper James Ducat, his first assistant Thomas Marshall, and supernumerary keeper Donald McArthur, taking a spell of duty in place of assistant keeper William Ross who was ashore on sick leave.

Right up to mid-December weather around the northern coasts of Scotland had been bad, but two days before Christmas it moderated, so that the *Hesperus* made fair time to a point less than a mile off the island where Harvey dropped anchor and ordered a boat away. Buoy master Macdonald, making a routine check of floating navigational lights around the isles, climbed the bridge of the supply ship and asked Harvey didn't he think it just a shade unusual there was no sign of life ashore? Harvey nodded; he reckoned this was the first time the supply ship had come in with a relief man aboard without one keeper at least emerging from the lighthouse to greet them. The *Hesperus* fired a recognition rocket, but received no answering signal.

Keeper Moore got into the ship's boat, stowed his gear and was rowed ashore; they watched him climb to the lighthouse and disappear; and they saw him come stumbling back, worried, puzzled. He told them that the Flannan Light was deserted; that an uneaten meal was laid in the living room, a chair was overturned as if someone had left in a great hurry; that an uncanny silence prevailed everywhere. Macdonald and Harvey shook their heads. Something had happened . . . but what? Buoy master Macdonald, with seamen Lamont and Campbell, volunteered to return to the island with keeper Moore and remain there until the whole matter was satisfactorily cleared up and the missing keepers located.

They reached the lighthouse, entered the duty room, examined the chief keeper's logbook. It contained normal entries concerning weather conditions, state of the lantern, supplies, a dozen other items concerned with maintenance *up to and including December 13:* and this was December 26. On a slate nearby, for subsequent transfer into the logbook, were noted the time of lighting the lantern on December 14 and extinguishing it on the morning of December 15, along with barometric and thermometer readings and the state of prevailing wind as noted by chief keeper Ducat at 9 A.M., December 15. Nothing more.

They climbed to the lantern gallery; the lamp was

45

trimmed, ready for lighting; oil supplies were plentiful, nothing appeared out of order. Obviously, normal routine had gone on to the morning of December 15, a fine, clear day with a lazy sea running and no hint of bad weather. But then everything had ended, and Flannan Island's three-man crew had left their posts and disappeared that fateful Saturday, in broad daylight.

A full-scale official investigation was made, with the finding that ". . . from traces evident of former bad weather conditions experienced in the area in the period ten days to the time of their disappearance, it must be concluded that the three men left their posts possibly to secure gear or to ascertain the exact extent of storm damage at the landing stage, and were there caught by an unexpectedly heavy sea and drowned."

The Flannan Island mystery was briefly reported in the newspapers—there were no headline stories in those days—and world events far beyond the lonely coast of northern Scotland eventually pushed the mystery right out of the press columns. But it was not forgotten among the superstitious Scots folk, the people who dwelt in crofts and cable fishing cottages, to whom the supernatural is commonplace. They asked each other whether Ducat and Marshall and McArthur, three seasoned lighthousemen, would have been fool enough to walk out one by one and never come back. The idea was preposterous.

Even if two had left, the third man would not have deserted his post. He had ways and means of contacting shore and calling for assistance. So it was rumored that

Ducat, maybe, or one of his companions, had sighted a ship in distress and gone to investigate; and when he failed to return, a second keeper had gone in search of him, seen the same distress signal, and disappeared. And the third man, puzzled and anxious, had followed in their footsteps. . . . The years slipped by and the unsolved mystery of Flannan Island would have been forgotten but for a poet who immortalized the strange affair. Not that Gibson's poem was to become widely known or read.

Aye, though we hunted high and low, and hunted every-
    where,
Of the three men's fate we found no trace,
Of any kind in any place
But a door ajar, and an untouch'd meal
And an overtoppled chair;
And as we listened in the gloom of that forsaken living-
    room,
A chill clutch on our breath,
We thought how ill-chance came to all who kept the Flan-
    nan Light. . . .
And long we thought of the three we sought—
And of what might yet befall!

World War I erupted, flared and died down; a post-war slump hit a world struggling to regain its feet, and the crazy twenties had fun and games until the bread lines lengthened. And then one fine April evening, taking time out and the weight off his feet on a bollard, port officer Kristan Jonasson idly watched two vessels steaming slowly into Reykjavik Harbor. He looked again, more carefully. What he saw was a local trawler

47

and, keeping its distance astern, towing a rowboat, he saw what appeared to be a Faroes drifter; in the boat were two men, one in a white oilskin suit, the second wearing black.

Jonasson strolled over to his small office, unhooked the telephone, and called the harbor pilot. He suggested contacting the port doctor to take a look at the crew of the second vessel which, so far as he knew, had never before come to anchorage at Reykjavik. The harbor pilot asked whether the drifter bore any identity. Jonasson said she did—the letters FD, denoting her port of registry as Fuglefjord. But her identification number seemed to be obliterated. Fifteen minutes later the port doctor and harbor pilot walked into Kristan Jonasson's water-front office and Jonasson jerked a thumb toward the vessel. The three men climbed into a police boat and cast off . . . and as the motor chugged into life the drifter bearing the letters FD disappeared into a haze. Copenhagen officials were contacted. They replied that no such drifter, no fisheries vessel of any kind or description, was anywhere in the vicinity of Fuglefjord or Reykjavik.

That happened in 1927, twenty-seven years after the Flannan Island mystery. Ten years later, to the day, another Scottish lighthouseman, Andrew Black—as level-headed a man as one could meet in a month of Sundays—"saw" a ship bearing the identification letters FD.

The one thing in life Andy hated and feared was that in some way he would become news. He had been chief keeper at Inchcape Rock Lighthouse, that wave-swept outpost, perhaps better known as the Bell Rock immortalized by poet Southey's saga of Ralph the Rover and the Abbot of Aberbrothock. During World War I when the British warship *Argyll* grounded and broke up, Andy helped rescue many of the ship's crew of nine hundred and fifty. To him, it was just another job of work; to newspapermen it was the kind of story war threw up once in a while, so they converged on Inchcape Rock.

Andrew Black welcomed them and took them around the back of the lighthouse to show them his pet donkey. There was, he assured those newsmen gravely, no other animal like Pat. He used him to carry stores from the landing stage, but just try to make him do more than his fair share, and what happened? Pat "just sits down squarely on his beam ends and refuses to move," explained its proud owner, adding, "I reckon it's the only donkey that can count. See what I mean?"

He refused to give them the headline story they sought. He hated making news; he was just another ordinary lighthouseman, he said. He was later transferred from Inchcape and given charge of the Pentland Skerries Light, a lonely outpost on a knob of rock right off John o' Groat's, in the extreme north of Scotland, in an area where tide races and vicious cross seas dragged many a ship to her doom. With his two assistants Andy made a snug home at nearby St. Margaret's and settled down to a hermit life; he preferred it that way.

He was on watch one wild winter night in 1936,

when he sighted a distress signal, a light that flickered, dimmed, flickered again. It came from the deck of a trawler in danger of being driven ashore; he called the mainland by radio telephone but received no reply. The shore operator had finished his spell of duty and turned in. By dawn, when contact was made at last, that Grimsby trawler had been smashed to pulpwood and every man aboard was dead. That experience hurt Andrew Black more than he cared to tell.

Twelve months later a Russian freighter headed into trouble off Andy's lighthouse and he waded chest-deep into wild seas and worked through the night and into dawn, until every member of the crew was safe ashore. Once again, keeper Black refused to give his story to hungry newsmen. All he had to say was that, coming ashore with an injured seaman, he was fool enough to lose his footing on slime-covered rocks and sprained a wrist. It worried Andy, for he wanted to be one hundred per cent fit for his job at any hour of the day or night.

And then it happened. . . . At the height of a violent gale piling seas up and around the lighthouse, Andy climbed to the lantern gallery and peered through night glasses. For a while he refused to believe what he saw: a ship with a white distress light showing from midships, and, for all that, battling her way through mountains of water, coming straight for the rocks in a superb manner. On such a night, no ship had the right to sail on this way, and yet show a distress flare!

Andrew Black stumbled down from the lantern gallery, called to his two-man crew, and told them what he had seen. Maybe, he reckoned, a trawler of sorts, though he could not define her size and shape, and she looked "a bit on the strange side." He ordered them to remain at their posts while he pulled on oilskins and stumbled out into the wild night, to the water's edge— and was gone.

No trawler, no vessel of any type, was anywhere near the Skerries Light that night; and no seaman had flashed a light in distress. At the subsequent inquiry, Andy's chief assistant told how he watched Black reach the sea's edge, swing his hurricane lantern, peer out to sea, then step by step continue on his way—*as if some unseen power was drawing Andy toward it.* Then a welter of seas roared in, and when it subsided Andy was gone. They found his broken body four days later on the Orkneys. . . .

A year after keeper Black went out to help the ship which had never existed, a British trawler fleet steamed through the Sound of Islay shortly before midnight. The weather was good, the seas calm as a mill pond; and the cook aboard a trawler, carrying hot coffee to the mate at the wheel, told him another trawler was coming down on the fleet. Had the mate seen her? He had not. So, challenged Cooky, the mate would not believe *this trawler was unmanned!*

Every vessel in that fisheries fleet sighted the strange ship whose funnel carried the black-white-red markings of a well-known fisheries company. Her registration number, plainly visible as the vessel sailed past the fleet, was FD-12. She sailed on and clean out of the Sound and vanished into thin air, and no such ship bearing that registration number existed or was registered in any European country.

Then came World War II. Around 1942 half a dozen ordinary little freighters loaded in the port of Lysekil, taking aboard vital war supplies of roller bearings, airplane tubing, small machine tools wanted urgently in British munition plants. They slipped moorings and steamed through that long, narrow strip of water stretching out into the North Sea, the Skagerrak. On the southern flank was Jutland, on the north the coast of Norway, and both were amply provided with Nazi air bases. They called that run "Hell's Passage." The Germans gave those freighters a name of their own; they called them "ghost ships," and rightly so, for no matter how hard they tried to intercept them, somehow they got through.

Sailing alongside the miniature convoys every once in a while went other vessels—very small vessels, with two or three, sometimes half a dozen men aboard. These were Norwegian patriots who had been in exile in Sweden, trying to make the North Sea passage so that they could join Norwegian forces stationed in Britain. For those very small ships it most certainly was the "Hell's Passage." Some got through. Others were not so fortunate.

In a flotilla of light naval forces we maintained patrol around the Norwegian coastline and south to Heligoland, probing the Nazi strength, keeping the enemy guessing and on his toes, giving them nightmares of indecision and anxiety. It was during one such patrol that one of the small freighters was bombed by the Luftwaffe. We picked up the first officer from among splintered wreckage that bore witness to the indomitable spirit which led men like him to make the attempt in the face of overwhelming odds. And that first officer told us the story of Falkenberg. . . .

It happened, he said, back in the twelfth century when, in the province of Limburg, near the present Dutch-German frontier, two brothers lived in the castle of Falkenberg; two presentable young men who vied for the favors of Alexis, lovely daughter of the Count of Cleves. The girl played one against the other, and in the end chose the younger brother, Waleran. On their wedding night, Reginald Falkenberg, the elder brother, concealed himself in their bed chamber and slew the young couple; and as Waleran died he reached out and planted one bloodied hand on his brother's face.

Overcome with remorse, the killer fled from the castle and sought a holy hermit living in nearby woods and asked to be absolved for his crime. He was told that absolution could not be given, but that he must journey northward until he reached the coast, where a sign would await him.

So he set out and reached the coastline, and there two dim figures awaited him and escorted him to a boat. One of those figures was clad in white, the other in black. They rowed Falkenberg out to a ship, ordered him to step aboard, and escorted him silently to a cabin. They sat down at a table—and commenced playing dice for his soul. They would continue to play, they told Falkenberg, to eternity; their ship meantime would ride the North Sea from the Arctic to Iceland, around Britain and back to the Barents Sea. Their vessel would change her appearance at will and, on being sighted down the centuries to come, would show a white distress light and lure ships and men to death and destruction. . . .

A strange story. Make what you will of it. Hundreds of men whose livelihood comes from the sea and whose ships fly the flags of the Scandinavian countries, Germany, Holland, Belgium, France and the United Kingdom have told stories of sighting Falkenberg's "ghost" ship and are ready to swear that what they saw existed, and exists to this day. The North Sea area in its most savage mood can mean hell for both men and ships, and in such times men's nerves are taut, reach the breaking point, so that imagination can play strange tricks.

In a long spell of life afloat, men find themselves on the edge of something far greater than shore folk ever experience. It is awe-inspiring, like being at the mercy of a greater Power who holds the destiny of seamen in the palm of His hand. In some men there arises a black feeling of utter evil. Maybe I'm wrong and it is not so; I think it is, for I have sailed with such men.

But there it is: Those three keepers who walked from their duty on lonely Flannan Island; the mystery ship that sailed into Reykjavik Harbor; Andy Black; the experience of the British trawlermen in 1938; and finally

54

the story we heard from the first officer of the ship lost on the "Hell's Passage" run. Conjecture? For myself, reporting all these facts as they are known and accepted, I maintain an unbiased mind—until someone happens along to convince me one way or the other.

4.

Terror of the Hungry Sands

THE torpedo got us clean amidships, just as the forenoon watch was handing over, just as we were climbing out of the engine room for a bath, a hot meal and warm anticipation of being tied up on the water front next morning, freed of duties for the best part of a week. It only goes to prove that you can count on nothing in wartime.

In convoy, we had made an uneventful voyage in a series of hops known to every man who worked the New York-London service; New York-Fire Island, 51 miles; Fire Island-Bishop Rock Lighthouse, 2,852 miles; Bishop Rock-Nab Tower, 256 miles, all neatly recorded in the ship's log; and now there was a mere matter of 500 miles or so to complete the trip. But that last hop meant—and we were all keenly aware of the fact—running the constant risk of being battered by German long-range guns located over on the occupied French coast. That, and marauding U-boats operating around the Dover Straits. In the end, a U-boat won out and we lost.

Any man who has served the sea either in peace or war knows that it has strange whims; once in a while it becomes catlike in cunning, and at times is a thing of foreboding and infinite evil. More so when fog comes down on a glassy, still sea and closes in like a pall; times like that a man's imagination can run wild and nerves reach breaking point, so that acceptance of the supernatural without pause or question is understandable. I write from hard experience, especially when it comes to shipwreck on treacherous sands.

The day was bright but cold as the convoy steamed eastward, nearing Dover, but there was an ominous hint of fog and we were of mixed opinion about that; if fog closed in, it could ease the tension of expecting attack from the skies, and enemy spotters over on the French coast would look for us until their eyes closed with fatigue and still not find us. On the other hand, fog would reduce our speed to a minimum, and that would mean we became sitting ducks for U-boats.

In our own ship, and others nearby, seamen were swabbing down decks, coiling ropes, easing hatch covers ready for tomorrow's unloading; and as they worked some of them took a quick look to the north, over to where land was faintly visible, but blurred and shapeless. Maybe what they saw was not the mainland of England but that ten-mile area every man who ever sailed through the English Channel always treated with great respect and feared. The Goodwin Sands.

In a split second, a smart freighter on our starboard flank suddenly reared out of the seas to show a gaping space between keel and foaming water, then heeled over and slipped from sight.

We thought it was a mine, one of the magnetic type in use during that period of the war. How wrong we were was hideously obvious moments later when the U-boat loosed a second torpedo and caught us, breaking the back of our ship, bringing the mainmast crashing down and killing the captain and first mate on the bridge. All around us seamen were scattered like human litter.

Five of us grabbed a floating hatch board; we were all half-naked, some were wounded. The rest were, I think, almost insanely defiant. The convoy had scattered, disappearing from sight, and we realized we were quite alone, and that the Channel had become glasslike and deadly calm.

Those of us capable of action tried paddling toward the mainland with our bare hands, but they soon became numbed by cold; and we drifted through that long night, until, as a blurred dawn broke, with barely the strength to lift our bodies from the hatch board we dragged ourselves onto a bank of sand. We seemed to be on the outer edge of the world we knew—a strange world with light and shadow playing macabre tricks. Just ahead of me I fancied I saw the outline of a fellow officer and called to him; but he was not there. It was odd, uncanny; I could have sworn someone, or something, moved wearily, silently, ahead of me. Days later I learned that my shipmate had died in the explosion of the torpedo.

I STILL LOVE MWR

A dank, gray blanket of fog penetrated our scant clothing, seeping into the very marrow of our bones. When we ventured to speak our voices sounded remote, as if from a great distance and from persons other than ourselves. If we moved, our shapes loomed twice as large as life, grotesque and frightening. By tacit agreement we ceased speaking and lay quiet, still exhausted . . . until, nearby, another voice in another language said something none of us understood. The speaker came nearer and was then joined by other vague shapes, caricatures of men who halted in a half circle and stood regarding us.

It was an eerie experience; still more eerie when one of those gray shapes laughed, a sound that still sends prickles down my spine when I recall it. But a moment later we were on our feet and everybody was laughing and greeting one another. The tension snapped. The spook world we had imagined ourselves in became real again; real and hard.

They were a tragic bunch of half-starved, red-eyed seamen. They told us, partly in sign language, partly by the few words we knew, that they were the last survivors of a Free French ship torpedoed earlier that week off Cherbourg; they had taken to the only sea-worthy lifeboat, fifteen men all told, without food or drinking water. Five had lived; the others, dying, had been pushed overboard. And these five men, like us, had drifted eventually onto the Goodwins. Like us, too, they had been scared; frightened by the gray silence that surrounded them when the fog came down; sus-

59

picious at first of our presence but utterly relieved when they knew we were living and not shapeless things come out of the sea. Maybe it all sounds fantastic, but it was the glaring truth to all of us that dank, cold winter morning.

It was my second experience of shipwreck; my second, too, of hungry sands that can swallow ships and men and soon leave no trace of either. The first occasion, in the years between World Wars, had been in a freighter bound for Baltimore. Southeast of Wilmington, Delaware, a crazy vortex of wind and sea we had successfully dodged for three days caught up with us, carried the ship triumphantly inshore, planted her squarely on a giant sand ridge and there cracked her open as easily as one opens a walnut. This happened on Diamond Shoals, the eight-mile area of sand where, in the last couple of centuries, the Atlantic, boiling over rows of submerged sand, has taken more than two thousand ships to their doom. There is, I submit, a strange likeness between Diamond Shoals and the Goodwin Sands. Shipwrecked on either, a man is liable to find himself in the presence of eternity, quiet and invincible—and, with fog, he feels a presence of something quite evil. . . .

Back in the tenth century, the Goodwins, extending northeast and southwest off the coast of Kent, were charted on maps as *Insula Lomea*, self-explanatory if ever a location was suitably named. The whole area once formed part of the estate owned by Earl Godwin who was held responsible by Edward the Confessor

HELLO PEOPLE OF THE 21ST CENTURY

for the administration of that part of the English mainland. During the Conquest Godwin's estates were seized and handed over to the Abbey of St. Augustine, Canterbury, whose abbot was ordered to build and maintain a worthy sea wall against encroachment from the narrow seas dividing England from France.

The wall was duly built but allowed to fall into disrepair, and in the year 1100 the Channel waters swept in and demolished the structure, flooding the ten-mile area. Shakespeare knew about the Goodwins, for in his *Merchant of Venice* he wrote of Antonio having "a ship of rich lading wrackt on the narrow seas; the Goodwins, I think they call the place, a very dangerous flat and fatal, where the carcasses of many a tall ship lie buried." Shakespeare might well have used the dread sands as the setting of a drama infinitely grimmer than *Hamlet*. In the early fall of 1959, naval geological surveys confirmed that the Goodwin Sands break down under analysis into sand, layers of peat, and rotted wood, mainly timbers of ships, then primeval mud to the sea bed itself. It is known, also, that the Goodwins shift position every so often and, between 1930 and 1959, moved a distance of around two miles.

Chroniclers of maritime history, Richard Hakluyt the most prominent, have vouched for all manner of strange incidents on the Sands; it was Hakluyt who wrote of the Spanish Armada which, on July 29, 1588, was routed by Admiral Sir Francis Drake with his fireships; and, so Hakluyt recorded, as the Spaniards fled panic-stricken, aboard one galleon the commander offered surrender to the English and was at once slain by a junior officer. The dead man's brother immediately avenged his death while the galleon, aflame from stem to stern, her guns firing distress signals, drove herself hard onto the Goodwins and there went to her doom. That particular incident was responsible for supernatural occurrences right up to now.

Little more than a century after the defeat of Philip of Spain's tall ships, on the night of November 25-26, 1703, Britain lived through a night of terror after the worst storm in recorded history had lashed the country and the seas around it for ten days. It was, wrote a contemporary historian, "not merely a storm but *the* storm, the Great Storm." Gales, sweeping across the North Atlantic, reached the west coast of England and ravaged the land day and night with unbelievable intensity. Nothing like it had ever been known before, nothing its equal has ever been known since. In ten days hundreds of persons were killed, homes vanished, cattle were swept away, entire townships, together with the first Eddystone Rock lighthouse outside Plymouth Harbor, were demolished.

Then on Thursday, November 25, for a few hours the intensity of the howling winds fell suddenly, the lull everybody had prayed for; but toward dawn, November 26, the full fury was again concentrated, and along the length of the English Channel and around the coast as far as Bristol, more than five hundred merchant ships were caught in the maelstrom and sunk. It was around the Goodwin Sands that the most fearful scene of all was played out to its grim end.

A squadron of thirteen ships of the Royal Navy, returning to Chatham, had ridden out the weather safely enough off Biscay and, taking advantage of the sudden lull, up-anchored and sailed eastward, following much the same track we in the convoy did nearly two hundred and fifty years later. But when the lull ended, they were caught in the ferocity of that hideous night. Four of the warships were driven hard onto the Goodwins. One went to her doom in Yarmouth Roads, another off the Nore, the remainder at points around the Thames estuary.

The Sands claimed the frigate *Northumberland*, a 70-gun vessel under Commander James Greenway, with a crew of 253; the frigate *Restoration*, Captain Fleetwood Emes, with a crew of 368; the frigate *Sterling Castle*, Commander Johnson, with 349 men; and the frigate *Mary*, with Rear Admiral Beaumont aboard, and a crew numbering 273. Of that fearful tally, only two survivors lived to tell their grim story—two seamen from the frigate *Mary*, who later told how, as their ship was driven onto the Sands, "a great warship of Drake's day, her sails tattered, burning from fore to aft and her guns firing, served by demented seamen, bore down on us, sailed right through our ship and finally disappeared before our eyes into the depth of the Sands."

Who could doubt their sworn statement? And who,

63

for that matter, doubted the word of the captain of a big East India clipper, inward bound for London, who neatly and concisely, conscious of its drama, recorded this entry in his ship's log:

November 28, 1753: At ten of the clock this day, while riding out bad weather off Goodwins, awaiting better conditions to continue our passage, an armed frigate came driving down on my ship, her masts gone, her decks and hull in fearful shape. It seemed to us all there could be no avoiding her coming athwart our anchor-chains with dire results, and I was about to order my first officer to slip our anchors when we made out the frigate for what she was. Her name became clear for all to read; it was *Northumberland*, and as she came on, sweeping down on my ship, we saw men running in panic about her main deck. She appeared to be unmanageable. We watched in horror, for the wind was not strong enough to place any ship in such condition, and then it pleased Almighty God the phantom, for such it surely was, steered contrary to our mounting anxieties to windward and so drove on clear of us, but no more than two ships' lengths to our leeward, and so disappeared in what seemed a dark haze. It was a spectacle far too terrible to dwell upon, to see this ghost of what was once a fine warship going to her doom a second time. We saw a little steady trickle of men leaping into the sea, one after another, but their bodies made no splash as they struck the waters. The cries of her spectral crew, the firing of her guns every half-minute for assistance, filled us all with dread and terror that my men, as I, were nigh dead with the horror of it all.

It was fifty years since the great storm had destroyed

the naval squadron returning to Chatham, the 70-gun frigate *Northumberland* among them; and from the frigate *Mary* two survivors had told how they had witnessed the burning Spanish galleon which drove ashore on the Sands in 1588.

In 1784, from the London River went the schooner *Lady Lovibond*, her owner-master, Simon Peel, infinitely proud of his smart craft but far more so of the girl he had married two days previously and who was making the voyage. They had wed in the little church of St. Katherine, near Blackwall Stairs, from which point Captain John Smith had sailed in 1606 to found the English colony around the James River, Virginia.

At the helm of the schooner stood first mate Joe Rivers, embittered to the depths of his soul, for he had been rejected by the girl who had married Peel. By midnight, the schooner picked up the serving tide off the Nore, rounded the seaward point of the north Kent coast, lay on a course that would take her safely past the Goodwin Sands, on to the Channel and westward to the North Atlantic.

In such manner, and listing gently, feeling the favorable wind in her canvas, the *Lady Lovibond* took the seas under her forefoot and, feminine-wise, went on her way. At dawn next day, she creamed the seas into a white plume to port and starboard, and, by breakfast time, Simon Peel's young wife was up and about, decorating their cabin for the belated wedding supper they intended holding that evening when the schooner was well away from land.

Toward sunset she was out of soundings; sailcloth was set for the night, deck chores were completed. It was peaceful, serene. But Peel was a worried man. Rivers had flatly refused to attend the celebration, preferring, he said, to take his trick at the helm and spend the couple of hours alone with his thoughts while the Peels and their guests were merrymaking.

Alone at the helm, Joe Rivers swore and spun the wheel savagely, conscious that he had not the same power over the winsome girl in the cabin. And at that moment the schooner drove herself hard aground, dug her forefoot into the sands, shivered to a halt and heeled over.

One seaman of the *Lady Lovibond*'s complement of fifty souls, clinging half-drowned to a broken spar, lived to tell his story. Washed ashore near Pegwell Bay and picked up and tended by local fisherfolk, he described the tragedy as he had witnessed it, shivering with the fearful memory as he spoke. He told his rescuers that as he came on deck from Simon Peel's cabin shortly after the celebration commenced, he had seen Rivers frozen with terror at the helm, staring at the apparition of a 70-gun frigate bearing down on the schooner. The seaman dived over the rail as the *Lady Lovibond* took her death plunge, and drifted ashore to the mainland.

Fifty years later the *Lady Lovibond* returned from the undersea world of dead ships and played out the tragedy of her last voyage to the bitter end; the phantom was seen, so they claimed, by hundreds of local folk on the mainland; and fifty years after that, the ghost ship is said to have appeared a second time and was reported by the captains of two passing vessels and scores of horrified folk ashore.

Maybe it is just coincidence; but on the night of November 26-27, 1954, another great storm swept its deadly path of destruction from end to end of the English Channel. That night seven men, the regular crew of the South Goodwin lightship, died. Only one, a British government research scientist, escaped to tell the tale, owing to a miracle rescue by an American helicopter team. The crew of the lightship were never found. When the seas abated, frogmen searched all that was left of the battered lightship, but their work proved fruitless. Once again the Goodwin Sands had claimed victims. . . .

In 1934, one of the Kent coast lifeboats was launched to give assistance to a ship reported on fire near the Goodwins; when she drew near enough, lifeboatmen could see a ship blazing fearfully; but as they watched, the leaping flames died down and disappeared and though they searched the rest of that day and through the night, no trace of a ship or wreckage was found.

Toward Christmas, 1954, when the memory of tragedy that had overtaken the South Goodwin lightship was still fresh, I visited the Goodwins area with a chaplain to the Seaman's Mission aboard a supply tender. Here witches, warlocks and mayhem were commonplace in the half-forgotten days of sail. More phantoms have been seen in these waters than anywhere else on the seven seas. . . . We headed into fog. After a while there was an eerie chill on the night air and we were forced to drop anchor.

As the gray dank closed in around us, somewhere out there we heard the twin screws of a big ship. The sound came nearer, passed us and receded into the opaque distance. Overhead the moon seemed to be looking down from the top of an obscure wall, and the few stars that had been visible moments ago were soon blotted out. We knew we were just one unit in a small armada of ships, large and small, that would find no escape until this evil blanket lifted. We heard the soft lapping of water around the ship's hull, the mournful bleating of foghorns, the sound of ship's bells. A long, threatening black shadow loomed suddenly across our bows and drifted silently by. And I recall thinking, what a setting for the supernatural!

A bell buoy tolled funereally nearby; it was as if we were in a tomb that narrowed with each passing hour. It was an uncanny feeling; more so when I heard a strange sound, like something infinitely evil crawling aboard along our anchor chain. But the captain of the supply tender grinned at me.

"You'd get used to it if you had much to do with the Goodwins," he explained. "That sound comes from big hermit crabs climbing the links of the anchor chain of any ship in these parts!" At that moment there was a long-drawn-out hissing which steadily increased in volume and erupted into an ear-splitting roar, a most terrifying noise. It impacted on the eardrums, shriveled

68

them; it blasted the human senses and then went right through the body. Hideous, it rose to a crescendo, fell away into silence, then returned. It was one of the group of engine-driven diaphones aboard the Goodwin Sands lightships. . . .

The fog lifted by dawn and the supply tender up-anchored and was on her way. The chaplain and I sat in the captain's room drinking boiling hot coffee; and he said: "Like all things of danger and mystery, the Goodwins always had a strange fascination. If any one area ought to be haunted, it's this." I believed him utterly. He went on: "As I said, I don't have any brief for the supernatural, but you can't argue with facts. And it was just that—hard fact—that sent mainland lifeboatmen out on more than one occasion to succor a ship in distress off the Goodwins when *no such ship existed.*"

Today, recalling that chilling experience on Goodwin Sands, after the U-boat torpedo got my ship, I can concede the point the chaplain made.

5.

The Legend of "Lovers' Light"

A VIOLENT northeaster had blown itself out through the long night, and, with the coming of watery dawn, the skies still looked threatening and mile-long seas still rolled wildly, crashing their bulk against the lighthouse, curling around its base, reaching for the lantern gallery.

One such sea pitted its strength against this man-made pinnacle, climbed its length and blotted out the dawn light. The chief keeper took a steaming copper kettle from the glowing stove and brewed a pot of strong coffee; then he set the table for a meal, stretched his long arms, yawned. He reckoned he could use some sleep.

He walked across the watchroom, peered out through the window toward Cohasset rocks, just visible through a curtain of spume, and watched the seas frothing across the teethlike ridges of Scituate and Cohasset as they pounded the kelp-covered rock into a shade of cream-topped dirty brown. Minot's Ledge Light was shivering under constant onslaught; and Minot's Ledge, the chief keeper assured himself, at times like this could easily be on the extreme edge of beyond, though Boston lay less than eighteen miles distant—Boston and its bustling humanity, its civilization and friendliness. Indians long ago had chosen a fitting name for this place when they came down to the rock ledge at full moon to pay homage to Hobomoc, the Evil One, the spirit responsible for all the storms and gales which made this part of the Atlantic seaboard a place to dread.

Another fifteen minutes and the chief keeper would ring the alarm bell to awaken his relief, who would be as welcome as a plump turkey Thanksgiving Day; meantime, he dug deep into a pocket of his reefer coat and produced his well-used bruyère. With a knife blade he scraped the bowl clean prior to charging it with strong tobacco; one of these days, ashore, he would buy himself a new pipe. He grinned at the thought. He had been promising himself that for many months past.

He knocked the worn bowl against a table leg and a sprinkle of black ash fell to the floor. From the storeroom below, the knocking echoed back, deliberately and distinctly. Tap . . . tap . . . tap. . . . As if somebody had picked up a signal and was answering it. He paused a moment, then knocked the bowl again; and again, back came those answering taps. Yet he knew no one was in that empty storeroom. . . .

For the average passenger in any ship, a lighthouse means home, or maybe a strange land—the end of a voyage. For the seafaring man, it is just the usual turn-around and another trip ended, another soon to begin. For the lighthouse crew, it is a house-with-no-corners; little more than a vertical shaft of stone with a lantern and hundreds of feet of prismatic glass that must be tended and washed and polished, day in, day out. In stormy weather, tremendous seas make the whole structure quiver. To men like these, it is a vital job of work, to be carried out efficiently the year through, giving passengers, seamen and ships a brilliant shaft of occulting light by night and a prominent fix by day, with a roar of warning from siren or signal gun when fog descends.

Noteworthy stories of the supernatural in light-houses.

There are three. Great Isaac, located thirty-five miles from Gun Cay, on the Bimini group of islands in the Bahamas; Minot's Ledge; and Flannan Isle, that lonely outpost between Scotland and the eastern Atlantic seaboard. Some twenty years ago a British writer incorrectly claimed that the Tuskar Rock Lighthouse, off the coast of County Wexford, Eire, was haunted by a strange and mixed company of phantoms. But in the area around Tuskar Rock, about one mile off the coast of Glamorgan, South Wales, according to legend, ghosts abound. The story, worthy of inclusion in this particular record, is best told as it was published in the mid-seventeenth century:

Walter, though some say George, Vaughan, was Lord of Dunraven; he was reputed to be an "ingenious" fellow, his great fault being inordinate vanity. Soon after he inherited his title and the family property, including Dunraven Castle, a ship was wrecked on the dangerous rocks near the castle. Taking a rope, Vaughan swam out to the vessel and by this brave deed saved the entire crew. The incident took such hold of his mind that he set himself to devise some means of saving life in cases of shipwreck. His scheme was laid, when completed, before the government, but in those days the powers that be troubled themselves little with such matters and the invention was rejected. This slight, as Vaughan considered it, touched him in his most vulnerable point, his vanity, and his resentment was such that it is said it altered him completely. He determined that if he could not make a name for himself in one way he would do so in another. He decided he would revive the hospitalities of the Welsh chieftains of old, and thus would his name be known far and wide.

He kept open house and gave himself up to a life of conviviality. He married, for it was necessary for his own sake to have a son to whom he could hand on his name, his inheritance and the fame he was determined to win.

The years passed, and his reckless prodigality soon told not only on his personal resources but also on the happiness of his married life; just when his eldest son was approaching manhood, Vaughan's wife died, of a broken heart it was said. She left him with the four sons, the youngest a child of four. His wife dead, his fortune wasted, Vaughan could entertain no more; his castle was almost deserted and his former friends all departed.

His oldest son and heir, realizing that his inheritance was gone, determined to seek his fortune in foreign

73

lands; the father most reluctantly gave his consent to this desire, but the parting between him and his son was affecting and seemed to revive Vaughan's parental affection which had been deadened by his life of constant dissipation. His one thought now was how he could retrieve his fortune for his sons.

A wreck occurring some days later served considerably to replenish his coffers, as property "cast up by the sea," it was said, had by right belonged to the lord of the manor from Saxon times. The jingling of gold coins, unexpectedly come into Vaughan's possession, upset the equilibrium of this now most unhappy man and suggested to his unhinged mind the possibility of making even more money by means of wrecking so that he might reclaim the estate for his sons. For the furtherance of this scheme, Vaughan sought the help and advice of a man of desperate habits living in the neighborhood, known as "Matt-of-the-Iron-Hand." This wretch had been captain of a pirate ship many years before and, on one occasion, the vessel had been seized by order of Vaughan, then a magistrate. In the taking of this ship a desperate struggle had ensued during which the captain lost one hand, afterward replaced by an iron hook fastened to the stump of the wrist. From that day this despicable ex-captain had earned a livelihood as a wrecker, but had never forgotten the grudge he owed to the Lord of Dunraven to whom he attributed his ruin.

Thus, though during daylight hours Vaughan and this ruffian were never seen together, it was rumored along the Welsh coast that they were constant companions by night; Vaughan spent most of the night hours in a cave near his castle, from which he had a boundless view of the ocean toward the west.

Some time later, one hot summer afternoon, while

Vaughan watched seaward, unknown to him two of his younger sons set out in their father's boat for the Tuskar Rock, some mile and a half distant from the mainland; reaching there they moored the craft and gave themselves over to the pleasure of a swim. But from the cave, Vaughan noticed that a wind was rising and clouds gathering; the sun, too, was sinking in a stormy setting. Suddenly, the ill-omened form of Matt-of-the-Iron-Hand was seen approaching; he advanced slowly, stopping every so often to shade his eyes as he looked intently out to sea toward Tuskar.

Vaughan watched the man carefully, then the scoundrel's face was seen to change, a gleam of exultation came into his eyes and he uttered a sharp cry. Only then did Vaughan see his boat drifting off into the stormy sea, and the awful truth flashed into his mind. His two sons were stranded on the Tuskar and no boat could reach them in time. Distracted, he rushed down to the foreshore and from the Rock his sons could see him as he frantically waved to them. They were beyond his help. The seas rose higher and higher until the two boys were overwhelmed and died before their father's eyes. The catastrophes of that fateful day were not yet ended; servants in the castle who had witnessed the tragedy rushed down to Vaughan hoping to help him attempt a rescue at the last moment, and they left the youngest son, still an infant, asleep. When they returned from the foreshore it was to discover that the baby had awakened and stumbled toward the head of the main staircase, down which he had fallen to his death.

The events of the day were considered in the neighborhood as just retribution on a man who had gotten his gains by luring seamen to destruction with false beacons. Some such reflections must have come to

Vaughan, for he next tried to turn over a new leaf, avoiding his associations with the ex-pirate and fixing all his remaining hopes on the long-expected return of his eldest son. Vaughan had suddenly become very old, and spent every day watching the distant horizon for the sails of the ship he hoped would bring his son back. Then, one wild evening he saw a ship slowly standing up the channel as though those on board were on the lookout for some creek or inlet where temporary shelter might be had, but the gloom of the gathering storm soon hid the vessel from sight.

Vaughan was conscious of a strange anxiety about the ship, an anxiety he could not understand; moreover, he was fearful of Matt-of-the-Iron-Hand, whose vindictive hate was now unmistakable. The night darkened and grew thick; the wind rose and drizzling rain set in. Vaughan had not been long in his cave before the false lights of the ex-pirate threw a lurid light across the breakers. Listening intently, Vaughan heard, above the howling of the wind, the crashing sound of a ship being thrown on the rocks, wild and broken cries for help; then all was still and silent. In some thirty minutes the wrecker entered the cave where Vaughan still waited and told him that the ship's crew had taken to the boats as soon as their vessel struck and that they had then been swamped by seas and drowned; all but one member of the crew had died. The sole survivor, Matt-with-the-Iron-Hand said, turned out to be the captain, who had said that he was a Welshman and a native of Dunraven.

"Were you able to save him?" asked Vaughan.

A devilish laugh was the answer as the wrecker thrust a death-cold hand into that of Vaughan. A gleam of light from a fire in the cave lit up a ring on the dead hand, and the father saw that it was the hand of his only son and the ring on that cold finger was the one Vaughan had given him the day his son sailed away seeking his fortune.

Matt-of-the-Iron-Hand had had his vengeance in utter and final completion; recognizing the captain of the ship as Vaughan's only remaining son, even though the sea had spared him, the wrecker had coldly slain him, and cutting off the hand with the distinctive family ring, had brought it to the stricken father.

There is a different story of Vaughan's eldest son; it was recorded in this manner:

After trading with success in foreign parts in his ship, the son took himself a comely maiden for wife and brought her with him on his next voyage after their marriage. During this voyage, however, the young wife died and her bereaved husband, knowing that sailors are superstitious about having a corpse on board ship, carefully doubled the body and confined it in a lead-lined box in his cabin. When at last he returned home he brought the box ashore and placed it temporarily in a cellar of the family manor house; then, pending the ordering of a real coffin, he carried the box late one night into a wood at the rear of the house and buried it there. As soon as the regular coffin was ready it was taken, with the help of a trusted servant, into the wood for the purpose of transferring the tragic remains into its proper receptacle. But the lead-lined box containing the body could not be found; nor was it ever found.

The supposition was that some man had witnessed the impromptu burial and, believing that the box contained treasure, had dug it up and carried it away. Down the years since that time the phantom of the young wife is said to walk the foreshore along the Glamorgan coast, sometimes dressed in black, sometimes in white. So firmly is this apparition believed in and locally accepted that a recent owner of the old manor house, to whom searching questions were subsequently made, claimed she was awakened very early one morning by one of her maids, who told her mistress that she must leave her employ that same day, as she had been disturbed in the night by the ghost of a girl clad in white who stood silent by her bedside as if pleading dumbly for help of some kind.

But now comes a more curious part of this story. Repairs were being carried out a few years ago to the stables of the manor house and, on removal of some stone flaggings of the stable yard, the doubled-up skeleton of a young woman was found underneath. It was at this place that the body of the young wife had been deposited by the thief, who disposed of the box for the value of its heavy leaden lining.

Well, there it is; dismiss it as legend, or accept it as fantasy of the semiliterate folk to whom, in the days of Queen Elizabeth I, the world beyond their immediate homes was unknown and mysterious and the supernatural was given credence. But the fact remains to the present day, around the lonely coastline of Glamorgan, South Wales, between the mouth of the River Ogmore and Dunraven Castle, and on Tuskar Rock, one and a quarter miles offshore from Ogmore itself, strange shapes have been seen usually immediately before the break-up of weather. These are the shapes of two boys endeavoring to clamber out of reach of the seas; of an apparition whose clawlike right hand was known and dreaded by the first earl; of a young man dressed in captain's rig of three centuries ago; of a girl in white and, finally, of a demented man who runs along the deserted foreshore and disappears into the driving rain. All these phantoms have been seen and reported by the crews of passing ships and by local residents around Glamorgan.

In the Bahamas, little that is legendary is connected with the strange story of the "Gray Lady of Great Isaac."

The lighthouse at Great Isaac, an imposing structure, standing 152 feet above sea level, gives a powerful beam of nearly half a million candlepower and, by day, offers a fix with its bright scarlet bands on white. It is the only tower in the Bahamas lighthouse system to be constructed of cast-iron plating. Its lantern weighs more than five tons, and it is listed officially as a "first order" light. Completed on August 1, 1859, Great Isaac has its own story of the supernatural, perhaps the strangest of all. The story is vouched for by Commander R. Langton-Jones, former inspector of the Bahamas Imperial Lighthouse Service:

It was the first light beacon to be erected in the Bahamas after the accession of Queen Victoria and thus it became known locally as the Victoria Light. In the *Illustrated London News*, September 24, 1859, there appeared an excellent illustration of the Cay and the lighthouse, together with a fully detailed description of the building operations. Over the old entrance door is placed a tablet giving the date of manufacture as 1856. It is of interest to note that when first completed the

79

tower was set up in Hyde Park, London . . . and, later, the component parts were shipped from England on board the barque *Hero* and upon arrival at Nassau these were stored there until engineers appointed by Trinity House, London, arrived to erect it. Certain of the parts were conveyed to the site in the fast schooner *Arctic*, one of the lighthouse service tenders. Some difficulty was experienced in obtaining a vessel large enough to transport the remainder of the tower, but this temporary problem was at last solved by the arrival of the British barque *Stanley*, which met the necessary requirements and was thereupon chartered for the work.

She was a strangely unlucky ship, for when discharging her freight of castings at Great Isaac, a northerly gale came up causing her to drag both anchors; her captain stated afterward that he had never seen such a sea running on the Bank, and in a vain endeavor to save his ship cut away her masts and did everything humanly possible to weather the storm. During that night the vessel drove ashore and, with a resounding crash, her side was ripped open by the outlying reefs. Her freight was salvaged, no damage being sustained by the lighthouse plating in her holds.

Some two years before the tower was erected, a terrific hurricane blew in from the south and passed right over the Cay, leaving in its wake a long trail of death and destruction. Innumerable ships were trapped in its path and sunk or driven ashore; few survivors lived to relate their experiences after this fury of nature had been unleashed on them. Shortly after the passage of the storm a party of fishermen chanced to be passing the Cay. The night was well advanced and the rising moon had just broken through angry clouds to cast pale beams slanting eerily downward and lighting the barren waste around Great Isaac . . . and above the moaning of the wind the men were suddenly startled to hear a series of uncanny cries.

Eyes straining shoreward, they were astonished to see a strange sight, in the shape of a white horse stumbling heavily among the jagged rocks. With much trepidation and fear the men shortened sail, swung their vessel inshore, and there decided to land and investigate further . . . and discovered the object of their search. Stretched on the barren ground lay a handsome white horse, its neck broken, dead. How had this animal reached the forbidding Cay? The men decided to search the foreshore and at a short distance from where the present lighthouse stands they were horrified to find the rocks strewn with mutilated bodies, some half-buried beneath the pathetic flotsam of a recent wreck, thrown up by the seas. The scene presented a gruesome last message of farewell from some unfortunate vessel which had been lost out in the depths beyond. And among the corpses, already stiffened in the cold embrace of death, was that of a young woman tightly clasping to her breast the body of a child. Closer examination proved that a miracle had apparently happened, for the baby was still breathing. Gently but firmly, it was released from the mother's grasp and careful treatment ultimately revived this small and lone survivor of stark tragedy. Strangely enough, the baby had suffered no bodily hurt, apart from some exposure, and it was subsequently adopted by a couple living in Bimini. The child was afterward taken to England. . . .

One night, during the month of November in the year 1858, a member of the working party engaged in the erection of the tower breathlessly entered the bunkhouse where his comrades were congregated and excitedly told them that he had seen, in the light of the rising moon, the figure of a woman in white making her way slowly among the rocks skirting the foreshore, stopping at frequent intervals as if searching for something she had lost. Upon his approach she disappeared.

At first his story was laughed off as a joke, but very soon afterward the foreman of the erection crew, who had walked to the sea's edge to watch a passing ship, was terror-stricken to behold suddenly the same uncanny and mysterious figure.

On various dates between the years 1858 and 1913 this supernatural occurrence was reported by a succession of lighthouse keepers. On repeated occasions the wraith was observed from the foreshore, and, at times, seen to hover momentarily in the shadow of nearby dwellings. The attitude of the pathetic phantom was always the same, that of eternally searching among the rocks, vanishing here and reappearing there, much to the terror of all who saw it. These appearances always took place at the time of a three-quarter moon and were at intervals of months and sometimes years. The apparition became known to all keepers in the Service, many of whom were in deadly fear of the visitations. In 1913, the chief keeper at Great Isaac was coming off watch shortly after ten o'clock one night, and as he slowly descended the spiral stairway of the tower he observed the white phantom moving toward him slowly, upward. Her hooded head was bent forward.

For some seconds he remained rooted to the spot, paralyzed with fright. Steadily the white figure advanced in his direction, but just as he was recovering his senses sufficiently to turn and run, the white figure moved away and then vanished.

The following year, 1914, a routine change of keepers took place, and the appointed chief keeper duly held a solemn committal service for the dead, at dusk, on that part of the Cay where the drowned had been washed ashore almost sixty years previously. This keeper is still in the Bahamas Lighthouse Service; strangely enough, the so-called "Gray Lady of Great Isaac" was never seen since the burial service was held. It is claimed that she was the spirit of the mother seeking her child from which she had been cruelly parted by death.

There is only one comment I can add to this astonishing story, and that is that the keeper in question still served in the Bahamas in 1944 and, so far as I have been able to find out, lived there in honorable retirement until quite recently.

A thousand miles to the north of the Bahamas, Boston provides a peculiarly tragic story of a haunted lighthouse.

Nearly three hundred years have slipped past since North River pilot Tony Collamore took his ship just a shade too near dreaded Minot's Ledge and crashed to his death with all aboard. It was the climax to a long list of wrecks which, year by year, added a gruesome tally. At that period, the rocks of Cohasset and Scituate, ugly ridges only a few feet submerged even at high tide, had no regular name, and not until Boston merchant-shipper, George Minot, lost a homeward-bound ship in 1754, on these rocks, was the evil ridge given its name. In the ensuing hundred years nearly eighty ships were lost, with their freight and four hundred lives.

The prosperity of Boston was threatened by this constant peril, and a public meeting demanded an immediate solution to the problem. In 1847, Captain W. H. Swift, United States topographical engineering expert, made a careful survey of this reef, studded with teethlike pinnacles and chisel-like ridges, and decided that the most seaward rock of the group was the most promising site for a beacon on an iron-pile structure.

Work was completed in about two years; the beacon rose to a height of 77 feet above high-water level, and a Fresnel lantern, with fifteen reflectors, was set in place. Ceremonial lighting of the lantern was scheduled for October 10, 1849, but on October 7 a violent gale swept the coast and sank an emigrant ship on the outer reef of the dreaded Ledge. That fearful night hundreds of helpless men, women and children died within sight of the mainland.

On January 1, 1850, chief keeper Isaac Dunham entered in Minot's Ledge Light log: "This evening the lantern was lit for the first time." Three months later, he wrote: "A terrifying gale has struck the beacon causing it to sway alarmingly as I make this entry. God will in His mercy still these raging seas, or we perish. Should it get worse, I doubt whether any of us will live to see the dawn tomorrow."

Dunham and his two companions lived through that fearful night, but the experience so unnerved him that he immediately petitioned the government to reinforce the tower to prevent its collapse; otherwise, he wrote, he must resign his post. Captain Swift was shown the letter. He derided Dunham, who quit. Swift engaged an Englishman, John W. Bennett, incidentally a relative of mine, a man who, for all his known courage as a seaman, had in fact never stood watch in any lighthouse and had no idea of the severity of weather around Boston Harbor.

As new chief keeper, Bennett took charge on October 7, 1850, and hired two new assistants, Joseph Antoine, of Portuguese extraction, and Joseph Wilson, an Englishman. Six weeks later, after prolonged severe weather climaxed by a howling northeaster, Bennett requested an immediate inspection of the entire structure. A committee that journeyed out to the Ledge and reached it during a spell of calm weather, reported that "nothing need be done."

The months of November and December, 1850, and March, 1851, produced two violent hurricanes. On Sunday, March 16, great areas of Boston were under water. Wharves and piers were pounded to matchwood by the raging seas. At two o'clock that morning Bennett and his two assistants were pitched out of their bunks when a monstrous sea struck the iron-pile beacon, then a rising wind brought blinding snow, obliterating the lantern frame. By dawn, the three keepers had decided to remain for safety in the uppermost part of the structure, though it swayed and rocked alarmingly. They removed their gear to the platform just above sea level and settled down to whatever fate had in store. But the hurricane spent itself without further harm. Chief keeper Bennett went ashore into Boston, claiming

85

that he wanted to buy himself a new boat. He never returned to Minot's Ledge, nor was he ever seen again by his two assistants.

That same night a second, more violent, hurricane blew up; Wilson climbed to the lantern and lit it, but discovered that his way back to join Antoine was barred by shrieking winds and raging seas; he realized that he could not hope to maintain any grip on the rungs of the iron ladder. So, wedging his body against the iron piling, he tapped a message to his companion below. When the tapping was answered, he prepared to spend the remainder of the night on his perilous perch. Toward one o'clock the entire structure threatened to collapse. Wilson increased the lantern light to full, tapped down to Antoine ordering him to start the alarm bell and keep it tolling.

Ashore in Boston, people watched Minot's Ledge Light vanish time after time as it was assaulted by curling mountains of water; they heard, too, the mournful tolling of the beacon bell. They could do nothing to help those two men against this mad elemental attack of Nature; they could only wait and watch and pray.

An hour before dawn Antoine and Wilson knew they were doomed. Wilson wrote a last message: "The beacon can't stand any longer. She is shaking three feet each way as I write. God bless you all." He placed the folded paper in a bottle and threw it into the boiling seas. It was picked up two days later by a Gloucester fisherman.

The central iron-piling support gave way. The

tower swayed drunkenly and in seconds it was all over. Minot's Ledge Light toppled and was gulped down by the raging Atlantic. Antoine's broken body was washed ashore on Nantasket Beach; Wilson, who managed to reach Gull Rocks, died later from exhaustion. On April 22, 1851, Captain Swift returned to the scene; it was a bitter moment. He had promised to build a beacon that would "last forever," and he had done his work well. The seas could not tear his beacon up by its roots, so had snapped the piles away like carrots, one by one.

In 1855, General Barnard, a great American engineer, drew up plans for a new lighthouse, along the lines of the famous Eddystone Light in the English Channel. The task of construction was entrusted to Captain Barton S. Alexander, of the Engineers, and on June 29, 1860, the last great granite block was swung into position and a trial test was made of the lantern itself. Official and ceremonial illumination was scheduled for November 15, and as the sun set that evening Minot's Ledge split the night sky with its vivid white beam. . . .

A succession of keepers had charge of the new Minot's Ledge Light between then and 1865. It was in that year that the chief keeper, referred to earlier in this record, knocked out the bowl of his old bruyère pipe on the watchroom table leg, and received answering taps from below, from the empty storeroom. Believing at first that his first assistant was awake and was answering his signal, he set the table for their meal. But the minutes passed and no relief appeared. Then he rang

87

the alarm bell and, to his joy, received an answering ring.

When his assistant appeared he told him of the tapping and the answering sounds. The other grinned and suggested he was overtired. But the chief keeper repeated the performance and, again, back came the responding taps. The two keepers went below and searched the storeroom. Back in the watchroom, they remembered Antoine and Wilson had passed messages by tapping to each other that terrible night before they died.

Other keepers have claimed from time to time that the phantom shapes of Antoine and Wilson revisit Minot's Ledge Light, always before a howling northeaster blows up, to warn all seafaring men of imminent danger. Many a seaman claims to have seen the ghost of Joseph Antoine clinging desperately to the ladder that served the original iron-pile structure and, as monstrous seas come sweeping in, they have heard the cry, "Keep away! For God's sake keep away. Death is here!"

Seas towering to a height of 230 feet sometimes crash against the light on the Ledge and curl up until they reach twice the height of the modern structure. But these days the lighthouse is operated automatically and has been unmanned since September 24, 1947. Its occulting flashes, once, then four times, then three, around Boston will always remain associated with the words they spell. I L-O-V-E Y-O-U. "Lovers' Light," they still call it. . . .

I went out to Minot's Ledge ten years after its great light became automatic. It is a cruel place for a seaman and it is not hard to accept stories of seamen who said they had seen the ghost of Antoine. Later that year I visited the keepers of another lighthouse, Tuskar Rock, located off County Wexford, in Eire. Right across the Irish Sea on a clear day one can see the dim outline of the Welsh coast of Glamorgan, where the other Tuskar Rock is located—the rock of the Dunravens.

It was a bleak, cold morning in March, 1957, and we sighted a strange-looking object bobbing around in the seas, coming nearer and nearer to the tower on each succeeding wave. We watched it fascinated. It was a floating mine—a live mine, capable of blowing the keepers on Tuskar Rock out of this world. It came on, careering on its crazy path, until it reached a point not much more than ten feet from the base of that tower. Then, quite suddenly, it reared up out of the seas and vanished.

Thinking back on all those experiences of mine, somehow I think I would prefer to face a phantom rather than sudden death in the shape of a Hitler mine.

6.

The Perfumed Ghost of
H.M.S Asp

ABOUT the only thing George Manley Alldridge and the paddle-wheel ex-mail packet *Fury* had
in common was age. Both were born during a pretty
difficult period in British naval history, when the country was slowly recovering from wars and facing a dim,
unpromising future at sea.

Alldridge entered the Royal Navy the day after his
fifteenth birthday and one year later was posted to the
Survey Branch of the Admiralty, where he served for
the remainder of his chosen career.

The *Fury*, a vessel of 112 tons, with 120 horsepower
engines, was 89 feet 7 inches long, 16 feet 3 inches in
her beam, with hold depth measuring 8 feet 11 inches.
She came off her shipyard cradles the year Alldridge
was born, in 1815.

Listed in marine registers as a mail packet, the ship,
little larger than a Hudson River tugboat, shuttled her
47-mile passage with reasonable regularity between

Donaghadee, on the thin tongue of land in the Irish Sea which curves upward toward Belfast Lough, in County Down, Northern Ireland, and Portpatrick, on the west side of a hammer-headed stretch of coast known as the Rhinns of Galloway, in Wigtownshire, Scotland, carrying the mail and a few passengers.

Old-time sailors, watching her go and arrive at the two ports, sniffed contemptuously, calling her a "tin kettle." Port workers said she showed her age, and claimed that they could smell the worms in her. More affectionately, those who saw a great future for steam-driven ships looked at her admiringly and said she was ageless, a wonder, for she was a symbol—she had been built at the time when steam had ousted sail.

Alldridge took seagoing life in his stride and, on June 1, 1836, shifted into the uniform of a sub-lieutenant, officially gazetted in that rank; it had taken him seven arduous years to step out of the rough-and-tumble way of a midshipman's life and he had reason to be proud of his achievement. He set himself the task of becoming expert in oceanography and naval survey and took his examinations in the manner of a young officer born to his work. Nobody ever said he was brilliant; he was just one of those solidly dependable youngsters who could be given a task and relied on to carry it out competently.

The years sped past, and in 1837, when Alldridge was twenty-two, the British Post Office offered the paddle-wheeler to the Admiralty, who took her over, renamed her H.M.S. *Asp*, and sent her off for overhaul, refit and fresh paint prior to joining the Survey Branch.

But there was something about the ship; something indefinable; something nobody who knew her history cared to put name to, or talk about if he could avoid it. In 1850, six years after Alldridge was gazetted full lieutenant, he was given command of the ship.

He packed his gear, traveled from his London home to Pembroke Naval Dockyard, as enthusiastic as any young officer taking over his first command. When he arrived at his destination and saw the *Asp* he gave an excusable sigh. She was no fighting ship. She carried no guns. There was nothing formidable in her looks. She was just an old paddle-wheeler, past her prime, perhaps, but shipshape for all that. She was exactly what she seemed—a seagoing surveyor's office. Indeed, but for the lavish gray paint from stem to stern, and the white ensign she wore in place of the civilian flag she had flown so many years, nobody would have accepted *Asp* as a unit of his Britannic Majesty's Navy.

Her new commander looked her over as she lay at her moorings, then stepped into the office of the Superintendent of the Naval Dockyard and introduced himself—and heard the astonishing observation: "This ship you've got yourself is haunted, but I don't expect anybody told you."

Between that day and January 6, 1870, Commander Alldridge laid the first submarine telegraph cable between Holyhead and Dublin, carried out surveys of the approaches to Liverpool; Milford Haven; Bridgwater, in Somerset; the entire coastline of Wales from St.

Anne's Head to Stackpole Head, Barnstaple Bay, Devon, and nearby waterways. Nothing spectacular. Just routine naval duties with a specialist slant which, in later years, especially during the two World Wars, proved of prime importance to every seafaring man whose life and safety depended upon oceanography and underwater and coastwise survey.

Three years before he was gazetted captain and placed on the Royal Navy's retired list, Alldridge peeled off his jacket, dropped into an easy chair, stretched his long legs, and reread a letter received that morning. It was a request to give an exclusive interview to a newsman from the Pembroke County *Guardian*. Like most seamen, Alldridge hated publicity and newsmen. He pulled sheets of notepaper toward him, dipped pen in ink, and wrote this letter dated March 15, 1867:

My dear Sir: I readily comply with your request so far as I am able, respecting the unaccountable "apparition" on board my ship. Call it a ghost or what you will, still I assure you that which I am about to relate is what really did take place, and much as I was, and am, a skeptic in ghost stories, I must confess myself completely at a loss to account by natural causes for that which did actually occur. Many years have elapsed since I served in this ship and I am unable to recollect all the dates with exactness, but I will give them as far and as accurately as I can now recall them. In the year 1850 the *Asp* was given me by the Admiralty as a surveying vessel. On taking possession of her, the Superintendent of the Dockyard, where she lay, remarked to me: "Do you know, sir, your ship is said to be haunted? I doubt very much if you will get any of the Dockyard men to work on her much longer." I, of course, smiled, and I said: "I don't care for ghosts, and I dare say I shall get her all to rights fast enough."

I engaged the shipwrights to do the remaining necessary repairs and refit to the vessel, but before they had been working in her a week they came to me in a body and begged me to give the vessel up as she was haunted and could never bring anything but ill luck. However, she was at length repaired, and arrived in safety in the River Dee, where she was to commence her duties. After my tea in the evening, I generally sat in my cabin and either read to myself or had an officer of mine (he is now captain of the *Magician*) to read aloud to me while I rested my eyes, which had been giving me some trouble of late; on such occasions we used frequently to be interrupted by strange noises, often such as would be caused by a drunken man, or a person staggering about, which appeared to issue from the after (or ladies', as it had been formerly, when the ship was on civilian service) cabin.

The two cabins were only separated from each other by the companion ladder, the doors faced each other, so that from my cabin I could see into the after one. There was no communication between either of them and the other parts of the ship, excepting by the companion ladder which no one could ascend or descend without being seen from my own cabin. The evening shortly after our arrival in the River Dee, the officer I mentioned was reading to me in my cabin when all at once his voice was drowned by a violent and prolonged noise in the after cabin. Thinking it must be my steward, he called out: "Don't make such a noise, there," and thereupon the noise ceased. When he began to read again the noise also recommenced.

"What the hell are you doing, steward, making such a damned awful noise for?" he cried out, and taking a lamp off my table rushed toward the next cabin. But he came back quicker than he went, and I asked him had he discovered anything or anybody; he replied he had not, but appeared to me to look strained. He recommenced reading and once more the mysterious noise began. I felt sure there was some drunken person there whom the officer had not noticed and accordingly rose and looked for myself, and to my very great surprise found the cabin quite empty!

After that evening, the noises became very frequent, varying in kind and in degree; at times it was as though the seats and lockers were being banged about, sometimes it sounded as though glass decanters and tumblers were being crashed together. During these disturbances the vessel was lying more than one mile offshore.

One evening I and the above mentioned officer went to drink tea at a friend's house at Queen's Ferry, near Chester, the vessel at that time being moored alongside the waterfront opposite Church Quay. We returned on board together about 10 P.M. While descending the companion ladder, I distinctly heard someone rush from the other cabin into the fore cabin. I stopped the officer who was behind me at the top of the ladder and whispered to him: "Stand quite still. I think I have caught whoever it was." I then descended into my own cabin, took my sword, which always hung over my bed, and placed it, drawn, in his hand, at the same time saying: "Allow no one to pass you; if anyone attempts to escape cut him down. I will stand the consequences."

I returned to the cabin, struck a light and searched everywhere, but nothing could I find to account for the disturbances, though I declare solemnly that never did I feel more certain of anything in my life than that I should find a man there. So there was nothing to be done but suggest, as men had said a hundred times before, "Well, that was the ship's ghost again!"

Often when lying in my bed at night I heard noises close to me, as though drawers in my dressing chest were being opened and closed, the top of my cabin washstand raised and banged down again, and a bed which stood on the opposite side of my cabin pulled about; while, some evenings, I often heard while sitting in my cabin a noise as though a percussion-cap were snapped close to my head. Also, very often (and I write this with godly and reverential fear) I have been sensible of the presence of something invisible about me, and could have placed my hand, so to say, on it, or on the spot where I felt it was; and all these things occurred, strange to say, without my feeling in the least alarmed or caring about it, except so far that I could not understand or account for what I heard and felt.

One night, when the ship was at anchor in Martyn Roads, I was awakened by the quartermaster calling me and begging me to come on deck as the lookout man had rushed to the lower deck, saying that the figure of a woman was standing on the starboard paddle box pointing with one finger to the skies. Feeling angry, I told him to send the lookout man on deck again and keep him there until daybreak, but in attempting to carry out my orders the man went into a violent convulsion, and the result was that I had to go myself on deck and there I remained until morning.

The apparition was often seen after this, and always as described to me, with one finger pointing heavenwards. One Sunday afternoon while lying in the Haverfordwest River opposite to Lawrenny, the crew being all on shore, and I being at church, my steward (the only man left on board) while descending the companion ladder was spoken to by an unseen voice. He fell down in terror, and I found his appearance so altered when I returned that I really scarcely knew the man! When he had sufficiently recovered he begged to be allowed his discharge from the Navy and to be put ashore as quickly as possible, to which I felt obliged to consent as he could not be persuaded to remain on board another night.

The story of my ship being haunted becoming known on shore, the clergyman of Lawrenny visited me one day and asked to be allowed to question the crew, which he accordingly did. He seemed very deeply impressed by what they told him; he seemed to view the whole matter in a serious light and said that his opinion was that "some troubled spirit must be lingering about the vessel."

During the years that I commanded the *Asp* I lost many of my crew, who ran away and deserted on being refused their discharge, and a great many others I felt forced to let go, so great and real was their fear, one and all telling me the same story, namely, that at night they saw the transparent figure of a woman pointing with one finger to the skies. For many years I endeavored to ridicule the whole affair as I was often put to considerable inconvenience by the loss of crew, but to no purpose. I believe that when the officers left the vessel after sundown none of the crew would have ventured into the cabins on any account.

One night I was awakened from my sleep by a hand, to all sensations, being placed on my leg outside the bedclothes. I lay silent for a few moments to satisfy myself of the truth of what I felt, and then grabbed at it, but caught nothing. I rang my bell for the quartermaster to come with his lantern, but we found nothing. This occurred to me several times, but on one occasion as I lay wide awake a cold hand was laid upon my forehead. If ever a man's hair stood on end, mine did then. I sprang clean out of bed; there was not a sound.

Until then I had never felt the least fear of the ghost or whatever you may care to call it; in fact, I had taken a kind of pleasure in listening to the various noises, and sometimes when the noises were very loud I would suddenly pull my alarm bell for the lookout man and then listen attentively to see whether I could hear the sound of footsteps or some attempt to escape, but there never was any, and I would hear the lookout man walk from his post to my cabin when I would merely ask him some question as to the state of the wind, or the prevailing weather, as a routine matter.

At length, in 1857, the vessel requiring repairs, was ordered alongside the dockyard wall at Pembroke. The first night the sentry stationed near the ship saw (as he later declared on oath) a woman mount the starboard paddle box holding up her right hand to the skies.

The phantom figure then stepped on shore and came along the path towards him, when he brought his musket to the charge and called: "Who goes there!" But the figure appeared to walk right through the musket, upon which the terrified man dropped it and fled for the guardhouse. The next sentry saw all this take place and fired off his own gun to rouse the guard. The phantom figure then glided past a third sentry who was on duty near the ruins of Pater Old Church; the man watched her, or it, mount the top of a grave in the churchyard, point with a finger to the skies, and then stand quite still until she vanished from sight.

The sergeant of the guard came with rank and file

to be told of what had occurred, and the fright of the sentries all along the dockyard wall was so great that none would remain at their post unless they were doubled, which they were, as may be seen from the official Report of the Guard for that night. . . .

At this point, I consider it justified to interrupt Alldridge's letter with this fact: On the occasion when only the steward was left aboard the *Asp* and went down to the cabin to investigate strange noises, as he stood silent and still, looking around him before returning to the deck, in the silence that prevailed he heard a strange, uncanny sound. The sound of distinct crackling of a woman's long hair as it is brushed on a cold winter night; he heard the strokes of a brush quite clearly, and, a moment before he fled, terror-stricken, he smelled the sweet, elusive perfume a woman might wear at a dance. As he ran for safety, the steward declared that he next heard the soft, taunting laugh of a woman, then a scuffle and a quickly silenced scream which ended in a fearful gurgling sound. Then all was quiet. I now take up again the letter Alldridge wrote:

Singularly enough, since that particular and very dreadful night, the ghost was not heard of again on board the *Asp*, and I never again heard the noises which before had so incessantly annoyed me. The only clue I could ever find to account for my ship being haunted is as follows: Some years previously to my having her, the *Asp* had been engaged as a mail packet between Port Patrick and Donaghadee. After one of her trips, the passengers having all disembarked, a stewardess on going into the ladies' cabin discovered a very beautiful

99

girl with her throat cut, lying in one of the sleeping berths; she was, of course, quite dead and, you will agree, rather horribly dead. How she came by her death no one could tell, though, of course, strict investigations were commenced immediately. But, and this is perhaps most strange: *neither who she was nor where she came from, or anything at all about her, has ever been discovered.*

All these unhappy circumstances gave rise to much talk, and the vessel was at once taken out of mail ferry service between Scotland and Ireland, and was not again put into commission until she had been renamed and handed over to me for the Survey Branch of the Royal Navy. Here, then, ends my story, which I have given in all truth. Much as I know one gets laughed at for daring to believe in ghost stories, you are welcome to make what use you please with this true account of the phantom on board H.M.S. *Asp.*

George Manley Alldridge, when he left the Service, retired to Paignton, Devonshire, and there died on March 21, 1905. The *Asp*, after serving for many years as an Admiralty tender for survey duties, was later employed on work in connection with Chatham Dockyard extensions, from 1869 to 1880; and there she was finally broken up in 1881.

7.

Soliloquy of a Traitor

HE STRETCHED his body on the trestle bed and closed his eyes. In two days and ten hours precisely, he would be dead, and trestle beds would no longer matter.

Some day, possibly, someone would make a study of his life and set down the story in a book; and people would read that book and there would be violent argument as to whether he was guilty of high treason and deserved the hangman's rope, or, as an ardent patriot, was worthy of kinder thoughts. A thin smile parted his lips; there was one incident no chronicler of his varied life would ever include: his meeting with a girl at sea. She was a quiet, lovely girl. . . .

In the last few days he had got into the habit of putting thoughts into words, mumbled words his two guards could not understand, and, even if they did, would not appreciate. The two uniformed men sat at a bare table in the center of the condemned cell, one of them reading, the other absent-mindedly shuffling a deck of playing cards. He watched them a moment, then closed his eyes once again, turned his head toward the bare wall and recalled the past as if he were a spectator looking at another life, not his own.

Shortly before his seventeenth birthday there had been a bitter showdown with his father to whom he made it plain he had no intention of entering the British Civil Service. He rebelled at the thought of that type of confined life, left home and got himself a job with a shipping company whose vessels served West African ports. He sailed out of Liverpool not as a seaman, nor in the engine room, for he was not built that way; but with a good educational background and what his employers described as "an engaging presence," he was hired as a purser.

Built in a British shipyard, of around 2,500 tons gross register, nobody could call the vessel by the more dignified name of liner. She carried mail and maintained a steady eight to ten knots, weather permitting, with freight and occasionally a few passengers hardy enough to make the voyage. Men who worked on the African coast were either crazy or had no real future in sight, for they faced constant threat of disease all along the coast, where many died from a variety of fevers. So far as crews of ships serving the coast were concerned, there was always an escape route . . . by way of the eternal bottle. Whisky was an important element in the lives of seamen working the coast service.

The purser's daily round of life aboard ship proved far from pleasant. From five in the morning, when the day watch turned out to holystone decks and swab up generally, the mournful tolling of the ship's bell, the incessant tramp of heavy boots, and the men's curses assaulted his ears until the hour when he climbed into his bunk and tried to sleep with the bulkheads around him black with cockroaches and numberless mosquitoes humming around his face. Added to these crudities, there was the stench of the bilges overwhelming him until his stomach turned.

Superintending the ship's galley was a man to whom cooking was merely a seagoing job, with no frills: salt meat, dried fish, dehydrated vegetables, cereals, syrup and molasses were his daily ingredients, and so he slung hash as well as the next man; whether his products up-ended the human digestion didn't matter to him. The captain was as tough as they come—uncouth but dependable though he boozed with every bit as much enthusiasm as his crew, encouraging them to drink as much as they could hold because the African coast drove a man crazy in time.

The purser stirred on the trestle bed, opened his eyes, looked across the cell; it was a grim, forbidding place, cold, utterly cold. He went back to recalling the events which had brought him here. . . .

It was Easter Day, 1916. John McCarthy, a Curraghane farmer, had come upon an abandoned boat and, nearby, a sheath knife, a box of ammunition, three Luger pistols, and maps of the nearby coastline. In the pocket of a heavy coat was a railroad ticket from Berlin to Wilhelmshaven dated April 12, less than four months since. That ticket was the main reason why the jury had found him guilty. Then there was that pretty little farm servant, Mary Gorman, who told the police she had seen him walking the road to Ardfert; and the police had finally cornered him in McKenna's Cave. He had told the sergeant his name was Richard Morton, that he was a writer, on his way from Dublin to Kerry.

They had taken him to Ardfert Barracks for questioning, but he had not given adequate answers; so they charged him with landing arms and ammunition on the Kerry coast. On April 27 he was brought to London to face a charge of high treason. They produced their host of witnesses, including repatriated prisoners of war from the German concentration camp at Limburg; men who had testified that he asked them to volunteer for enlistment in an Irish brigade to fight against "the common enemy," the English. Each volunteer was promised, when the war was won, a bonus of $100 and a free passage to the United States. The evidence had piled up against him.

Two eminent British judges summed up and, at 3:48 P.M., June 29, the jury returned their verdict: "We find the prisoner guilty of high treason. . . ." He was sentenced to die by hanging. An appeal was made, with a petition for mercy lodged by writers and intellectuals, but with no success. The British government had stripped him of honors awarded for outstanding service in Central and West Africa. And now he awaited the dawn of August 3. Born on September 1, 1864, he would have been fifty-two twenty-eight days after the noose was placed around his neck. . . .

Little more than ten years before he was hanged in Pentonville Prison, dishonored, disgraced, a man whose name was to become a byword wherever the English language was spoken, he figured in a book written by Sir William Brandford-Griffith, C.B.E., a legal expert in West Africa. I quote the extract from *The Far Horizon: Portrait of a Judge:*

In August, 1884, my wife joined me on the Coast; we had not seen each other since the day of our somewhat hurried wedding in England. She did not have a pleasant or a happy voyage.

In spite of her grave demeanor and scholarly gifts she was a shy, pretty girl, quite ignorant of the world and its rougher inhabitants. After the ship left Canary she was the only passenger left on board. There were no stewardesses; luxuries like that were then quite unknown, and any woman crazy enough to make her way out to such an undesirable place as West Africa was not likely to need any special comforts so it was thought.

Aboard the ship there was only one person in whom she could place any trust, and that was the purser, quite young, in his early twenties, soft-hearted and charming; he did all he could in his very limited way to make my wife's lot a trifle easier.

But what was in fact a gang of seasoned "coasters," tough, uncouth seamen, cheered themselves on the voyage with the contents of numerous bottles; and the captain was little better than his crew. It was a shocking experience for a young girl making her first sea passage; eventually, conditions on board, added to the climate, began to tell on her and she started a low fever and became so weak and helpless that she lay quietly in her cabin and watched the long hours go by. Deeply religious, she derived comfort from prayers, and they were to be answered in a strange manner.

The long nights were worst for her; in her cabin she could hear heavy footsteps on deck and loud voices as seamen passed on their duties and terrified her with ribald and gross jests and obscene laughter. She heard them laying bets as to whether their female passenger would ever reach her destination alive, and worse. It was a fearful experience.

But a few nights before the ship reached Accra, and at a time when things were at their very worst for her, shortly after darkness had fallen with tropical speed, the silence out on deck was broken by the heavy breathing of some animal. My wife made her way to the cabin door and opened it, fearful of what she might see, and there was the dark shape of a huge dog, lying on the deck. It looked up at her and thumped the deck with its tail, like any dog will when it meets a person it can trust and wants to be friendly with. It seemed to be trying to help her. Quietly, she closed the door, returned to her sleeping berth and for the first time in many days fell unconscious with a feeling of strange security.

The dog was gone in the morning, but it returned each night thereafter and took up its position outside my wife's cabin door. The reassuring thump of its tail whenever she looked out at it gave her renewed courage and increasing stamina. She picked up amazingly and though she looked thin and pale on her arrival her recovery had been truly miraculous. The ship's purser told me later that he was quite certain she would never survive the voyage.

She told me, on reaching our home, that she would have liked to see her canine fellow passenger, but in the bustle of disembarkation that had not been possible; nevertheless she declared she owed her life to the dog. We decided to invite the young purser to lunch with us on his return voyage to the coast, and it was then my wife said she meant to ask him about her strange comforter and protector; but I persuaded her not to raise the subject as the memory of her distressing voyage was best forgotten.

While we were seated at table, our guest said: "It was too bad that you should have undergone such a dreadful experience. I wish I could have done more to help. The captain is a difficult man, with a vile temper, especially when he has been drinking heavily. Our previous voyage was no better, and on that occasion, in a drunken fit, he shot his dog merely because it insisted on following him around the ship. It was a splendid animal."

My wife said, "What a shame, to kill any faithful dog. Tell me, what breed was it?" The purser remained silent and appeared not to notice her query. She continued, pressing the point: "As a matter of fact, I wanted to ask you about the dog that sat outside my cabin at nights when I was so ill. It gave me great comfort and courage. I really don't think I could have managed to live without its nightly presence."

Our guest put down his glass abruptly and looked steadily at her; he was very white and asked what she meant. She replied quite simply: "It was a Great Dane, wasn't it? I mean the one which helped me so much."

He answered her: "There was no dog at all on the ship when you made your voyage out here, let alone—" and here he stopped abruptly as if he was fearful. I knew then; so did my wife. We never mentioned the matter again. I have definitely unsympathetic views on all matters relating to the supernatural, but there it was; but for the presence of that great ghost of a dog my wife might never have rejoined me alive. I can only add a quotation from Kipling: "This tale may be explained by those who know how souls are made and where the bounds of the possible are put to." The words seem peculiarly apt.

In October, 1959, *The Black Diaries*, by Peter Singleton-Gates and Maurice Girodias, was published. It was a psychological case book, a record, scarcely relieved by any touch of emotional introspection; it was a damning indictment of a man who turned traitor and paid the extreme penalty for his acts. That man was Roger Casement, deprived of his title before he was hanged.

Shortly before writing this chapter I contacted an expert on such matters as this, and give the verdict as follows:

> In view of the many hundreds of vile acts Casement is said to have committed in England, Ireland, the Congo, on board ship and in South America, it is an interesting point that he was the only decent man on that ship. It strikes me it might be of some psychological significance if one wished to be very subtle and suggest that the ghost dog only turned up to help the poor young wife, because, in fact, Casement was anxious about her but obviously couldn't do much to help her. That is to say, his own watchdog instincts roused in her behalf released this phantom dog to help her. Casement would, I think, have been a little in love with the girl, but too violently inhibited for this to be possible. Who knows?

108

Roger Casement, rebelling at his father's wish that he should enter the British Civil Service, in the end found that destiny took him there, thence to the gallows. So far as I have been able to ascertain, he never told his story of the phantom Great Dane, though he could never have forgotten it.

8.

Paradox of the Pacific

IF EVER an area of the seven seas was jinxed it is that ill-shaped oblong between Okinawa, in the Ryukyu Archipelago, Disappointment Island, just south of the Marquesas, Hawaii and the Solomon Islands; for nearly three centuries it seems to have been the favorite haunt of ghost ships and spook sailormen.

No man has greater faith in Providence, no one believes so steadfastly in the powers of good and evil, good and bad luck, than the average seaman, and not without reason, for strange, unaccountable things happen at sea. Ships, like men, possess character of their own. They are created; they live; they die. During their life, some give dependable, uneventful service; some are a joy to serve in. Others develop a sinister streak, and follow a short, distinctly evil career.

In a previous book* I wrote of the sailing ship *General Grant*, out of Melbourne, Australia, bound for London. Under Captain Loughlin, a dependable navigator, she maintained her course from the day of her de-

* *Last Voyage*, 1958.

parture, May 4, 1866, until May 13; then, for no apparent reason, for she was in a wide region of good trade winds, she found herself becalmed, her canvas limp and lifeless, not a whisper of wind anywhere. Yet she drove on as if impelled by some unseen force, and so piled herself into a monstrous cavern under the tall headlands of Disappointment Island.

Nothing could save her from complete destruction; nothing was left of her, not even a spar, a remnant of sail, a hatch board, to show where tragedy had overwhelmed her. Men who knew her from the day she first slipped down the shipyard cradles shook their heads. They claimed that Loughlin, his officers and crew "signed their own death warrants the day they first took her out." There was mystery and to spare about the *General Grant*. The question is—*did she become a killer?*

Locked away in Loughlin's cabin safe was gold dust valued at more than a million dollars, consigned to London agents. Among her passengers, most of whom had made sizable fortunes in the Australian gold rush, was more precious metal worth at least another couple of million. What more attractive prize for salvage work?

Various expeditions were organized and went out to seek the treasure, but none ever made it. In March, 1870, the 48-ton schooner *Daphne*, with David Ashworth, one of half a dozen survivors from the *General Grant*, aboard, sailed out of Invercargill under her owner-skipper, Captain Jim Wallace, reached Disappointment Island and dropped anchor. Wallace, Ashworth and three seamen put away in a boat, located the cavern, entered it—and never returned. When the schooner finally made her home port, the survivors from her crew declared that as she lay anchored awaiting the return of Wallace, a spectral ship appeared, bore down on them, almost came alongside, changed course and crossed the *Daphne*'s bows, then appeared to dissolve in a gray haze.

Nobody believed their story. Men who had suffered a shock as they had, it was suggested, were "liable to imagine things." Yet there was nothing imaginative about the salvage expedition that sailed from London in 1958 and, in some unaccountably miraculous fashion, lived through a nightmare experience. Nor was there any imagination about a formal entry in the official log-book of the British warship *Bacchante*, in which, at the time, the late King George V and his brother were serving as midshipmen. The matter-of-fact phrasing of the entry, with its complete lack of the dramatic, bore testament to at least one phantom ship said to haunt this area between Okinawa, Disappointment Island, Hawaii and the Solomons. The *Bacchante* was homeward bound from Melbourne for England; and her log read:

July 11, 1881. During the middle watch the so-called *Flying Dutchman* crossed our bows. She first appeared as a strange red light, as of a ship all aglow, in the midst of which light her masts, spars and sails, seemingly those of a normal brig, some two hundred yards distant from us, stood out in strong relief as she came up. Our lookout man on the forecastle reported her as close to our port bow, where also the officer of the watch from the bridge clearly saw her, as did our quarterdeck midshipman, who was sent forward at once to the forecastle to report back. But on reaching there, no vestige nor any sign of any material ship was to be seen either near or away to the horizon. The early morning, as the night had been, was clear, the sea strangely calm. Thirteen persons altogether saw her, but whether it was the *Flying Dutchman* or one of the other few alleged phantom ships which are reputed to haunt this area must remain unknown. *Tourmaline* and *Cleopatra*, which were sailing on our starboard quarter, flashed signals asking whether we had seen the strange glow, and if we could account for it.

During the forenoon watch the seaman who had this morning first reported this phantom vessel fell from our foretopmast crosstrees and was killed instantly. Toward the end of the afternoon watch, after quarters, our ship was hove-to with headyards aback while we buried him. He was a smart royalyard seaman, one of the most promising hands in the ship, and every man on board feels sad and despondent at his loss.

That was not the end. When the squadron reached port the commander was stricken with a fatal illness.

Exactly what manner of spectral ship was this? She has been claimed as a four-master, as a schooner, as a brig; she is the *Flying Dutchman*, the wraith of a Dutch East Indiaman, and the *Libera Nos*, once commanded by Captain Bernard Fokke, who, in order to make port in record time, was said to have diced with the devil himself, and lost; since that day, his so-called "Ship of Death," with a crew of skeletons, is said to sail this region of the Pacific seeking ships to send to their doom. The *Libera Nos*, alleged to have been sighted on a number of occasions down the years, is reported to have a skeleton master standing on her fo'c'sle head holding an hourglass and timelessly marking off the centuries.

Whichever phantom it is, whatever shape or rig, if she crosses the bows of another vessel it means disaster and tragedy.

Vanderdecken, a violent, evil-tempered captain, is alleged to command the *Flying Dutchman*, though that was not the name she bore on her stern. The old legend has it that while rounding the Horn, bound for Pacific ports during terrible weather, Vanderdecken drove his ship like a man demented. Passengers and crew pleaded with him to shorten sail, ride out the gale, but as the seas smashed in at the ship and shrieking winds tore the sails to ribbons, Vanderdecken took over her wheel, lashed himself to the spokes, defied the Almighty to force him to ease up. Speechless with terror, his passengers huddled together in the lee of a deckhouse and watched. At a moment when the vessel seemed doomed, a brilliant shaft of light pierced the lowering clouds, illuminated the forecastle and revealed the figure of the Holy Ghost.

Vanderdecken surveyed the figure calmly, then snatched a pistol from his belt and fired; his arm fell paralyzed at his side, and he heard a voice saying:

"For your defiance of the wrath of God, such as you have displayed in this tempest which rages about your ship, you shall be condemned to sail the seas unto eternity. You shall remain at the wheel until both heaven and earth shall vanish. You shall never sleep, but will

114

maintain eternal watch where you stand. Food nor drink shall pass your lips, yet you will thirst and hunger. You shall never know calm seas again but will sail through tempest without ever reaching port. And henceforward you shall be the foreteller of misfortune to all who may sight you. In such way, sail on to the very end of time!"

This is the time-honored legend of the *Flying Dutchman*. By all modern standards it is fantastic, yet it is founded upon fact. Somewhere around 1660 a Dutch vessel bound for the Pacific was lost without trace of ship, passengers or crew. She was sighted last as she rounded the Cape, heading west; weather was good, the seas calm. So much is known and accepted as fact from reports made by the masters of two passing ships sailing before favorable winds; yet it was said that Vanderdecken's vessel appeared to be caught in a violent gale and battled her way through until there was no more sight of her.

Apart from her appearance to those aboard the warships *Bacchante*, *Tourmaline* and *Cleopatra*, the *Flying Dutchman* was reported by many other ships. In 1905, a homeward-bound Australian captain logged her as "painted bright yellow, low at the stern, with a double poop, one above the other, with three masts each carrying a turret lookout and what sails she wore hung tattered from square yards."

She was seen in 1893, when a clipper bound for New Zealand ports sighted the phantom off South Island, and at first took it to be a disabled "Blue Nose" packet.

In a London newspaper, in 1911, she was reported making an appearance before a whaling ship which the phantom nearly ran down. But one of the most authentic stories was given toward the end of the last century. Strangely enough, it centered around another lost treasure ship.

This was the steamship *Hannah Regan*, homeward bound with mixed freight and around a million dollars' worth of gold; off Okinawa she lost her propeller and then was badly damaged during heavy weather. According to later reports, her captain first tried to beach the vessel, but failed; then, with jury-rig sails, endeavored to make port. The propeller shaft came adrift, fractured her hull and sent the ship into deep water. Her log, with the bodies of captain, first mate and four of her crew, drifted ashore in an open boat some weeks later.

Salvage operations were planned, and a well-equipped ocean-going tug sailed from San Francisco, located the wreck lying in not more than ten fathoms, her stern held fast on a rock reef. Preliminary work cleared a way for salvage operations and plans were made to get down to the gold next morning. From this point the story is taken up by her captain:

It was a fine, calm and clear night, and after the days of hard exertion by all hands I had ordered them to rest before the arduous work that would be expected of us the following day. I myself was about to retire to my own cabin and snatch a few hours sleep but I felt the need of a quiet walk around the deck. I had taken a couple of turns, and could see in the bright moonlight our marker buoys locating the wreck, and was thinking of the tragedy that had overwhelmed her and all aboard when my attention was drawn to what I at first thought was a peculiar shadow some half-mile distant from my ship. I watched it closely for some time and then, to my astonishment, the shadow assumed the shape and appearance of a sailing vessel, clearly distinguishable but of a type which had not sailed the seas for at least two hundred years. There could be no mistaking it. She was headed in our direction, and driving along as if in the grip of violent winds, yet she carried no sail. I stood spellbound. She rolled heavily at times though the seas were flat calm; and she looked to be sinking by the stern. I was about to shout, to summon help, for it looked as if she could not help running us down, but then it flashed in my mind that this were a phantom and no material vessel. Had I given way to impulse and summoned my crew my action would have ended either in general fear of this apparition, or, if my imagination were in control of my senses, then I would be laughed to scorn. So I held my peace, but continued watching. The spectral ship came on, her starboard quarter almost awash and with masses of heavy water pouring over her. She came right alongside, and then I doubted my own shocked senses, for I could see right through her, though every detail of her deck work and her rigging stood out clearly. Two of her boats were hanging from their falls and dragged alongside; so she passed us by, still lower at the stern, and in such way *disappeared beneath the sea.*

Without knowledge of the overnight incident, the salvage crew assembled shortly after dawn and got to work, watched by their skipper, who again takes up the story:

This was no simple job, though the wreck was lying in less than ten fathoms, the seas crystal clear so that I was able to watch my divers. I saw one man like a cat climbing a sloping roof haul himself carefully along the broken hull, hand over hand. He made it. With him he carried a charge of gun cotton to breach the jammed door of the captain's cabin and so get at the safe containing the bullion. He disappeared from my sight and seconds seemed to drag past like minutes, the minutes into hours, and still no sign of the diver, still no explosion I waited for. A second diver went down to investigate, and some time later surfaced to report that the first man's airpipe had become entangled in wreckage and had been cut. The second diver returned to help his comrade, and we waited for two heartbreaking hours before we were ready to acknowledge their death.

The salvage attempt was abandoned that day, and the ocean-going tug returned to San Francisco, leaving all that was left of the *Hannah Regan* and her gold to be torn apart by the seas. . . .

The *Flying Dutchman*, the *Libera Nos*, or the *San Sebastian*—New York-built would-be speed-maker, launched in 1854 and last heard of off the Horn ten years later and, for some unknown reason, never officially registered in any port; these three spectral vessels are said to have haunted the Pacific for upward of three centuries, *and still do*. Still? My authority is Karl Doenitz, former commander in chief of Hitler's U-boats, the man who told his crews, "Kill, kill, kill! Show no mercy to enemy or neutral alike!"

Said Doenitz: "Certain of my U-boat crews claimed

they saw the *Flying Dutchman* or some other so-called phantom ship on their tours of duty east of Suez. When they returned to their base the men said they preferred facing the combined strength of Allied warships in the North Atlantic than know the terror a second time of being confronted by a phantom vessel." Maybe it is significant that almost every one of those U-boats met with disaster on their subsequent tours of duty.

9.

Hoodoo of an Atlantic Liner

STRANGE, how the attempt of a man with vision to jump the gun resulted in a white elephant of the seven seas—and a ghost . . .

For a dozen years, American and British shipping interests and governments, with what seemed utter contempt for cost, had slugged it out for supremacy on the world's most lucrative trade route, the North Atlantic. Since 1840, two main contestants, Massachusetts-born Edward Knight Collins and Newfoundlander Samuel Cunard, firmly established in London, each with government financial blessing, had planned, built and launched ships capable of clipping off the odd hour or two in crossing from New York to Liverpool, Boston to London. Their ships ranged from the earlier 1,100-tonners of Cunard to the Collins newcomers of around the 3,000-ton mark.

Neither side appeared to be getting anywhere. Meantime, Washington and London glowered at each other across the 3,000-mile expanse of sea.

To a man like Isambard Kingdom Brunel the whole

setup was crazy. There was no real vision displayed by either contestant, nothing was really accomplished. They just went on battling it out the hard way.

Brunel considered the matter carefully from every angle. It was all so very simple; a really large ship could do the work of two smaller, and cost less to operate, provided of course that the larger vessel was designed and built attractively enough to enjoy a full passenger list, with her holds packed tight with profit-earning freight each voyage.

If a shipbuilder constructed a fine liner, an elegant ship, twice the size of those Collins and Cunard were operating, her money-making capacity would be stepped up not twice but fourfold. Another point: it was clear that if a man designed and built a ship twice, maybe three or four times, larger than any Collins or Cunard had on the North Atlantic service, and once her engines got her moving through the seas, the larger ship would overcome atmospheric and water resistance far easier than a smaller vessel. Carrying four times as many passengers and freight as two smaller liners traveling at the same speed, she would be cheaper to operate and would show much larger profit. It was as simple as that.

Collins' record makers, the *Pacific* and the *Arctic*, both measured 2,860 tons; Cunard's largest was of the same tonnage, though Cunard had plans to build a 3,300-tonner. However, she would not be ready for two to three years. In that time, with larger, swifter ships, the world would rapidly shrink in size.

Brunel had decided on building a giant liner, the largest in the world—20,000 tons gross, with a displacement around the 35,000-ton mark. She would make anything the main contestants now possessed, or dreamed of building in the foreseeable future, appear dwarfed.

Successful builder of bridges and railroads, Brunel sketched his rough plans, then visited London's most famous shipbuilder. No time was to be lost. He said: "We will put this new ship of mine on the London-Australia service and there attract so large a portion of the world's traffic on this long haul as to make certain of full freights and passenger lists at highly remunerative rates both outward and homeward." He registered his company, the Great Eastern Steam Navigation, guaranteeing shareholders 40 per cent dividends.

A doubter queried his ideas about size. Brunel told him, "The *Great Eastern* will be at least twenty-five thousand tons." The questioner raised his eyebrows. "But why stop there? Why not make it one hundred thousand tons?" Brunel grinned. "Maybe I'll take you up on that idea."

Slowly, his monster ship took shape—608 feet long, 80 feet in the beam; her hull would be divided into ten separate compartments of 60 feet each by using transverse bulkheads, then those ten would be subdivided into thirty-six, and the whole lot would be enclosed in a double hull, so that there would be two ships, one within the other, all constructed of cellular steel framing.

That double hull—two iron "skins" three feet apart, one ship within another—was Brunel's master stroke, revolutionary, something never visualized before in world shipbuilding—a hermetically sealed compartment that would extend from the great keelplate up to deep-sea water line.

Into this enormous hull he provided for ten vast boilers, fed by 112 furnaces; to carry away furnace smoke there would be five tall funnels, towering toward the skies like huge fingers. The boilers would generate steam power amply sufficient to turn two 58-foot paddle wheels and, in addition, an auxiliary 24-foot propeller. Working normally, Brunel predicted, those boilers would comfortably produce around 15,000 horsepower.

The average mind was staggered by these facts and figures; a contemporary historian wrote: "We are lost in wonder at the amount of mechanical power which will thus be brought into play in the propulsion of one vessel, and the smoothness and harmony with which that duty will be performed, in a space necessarily confined and limited and amid all the violent turmoil of the ocean. No work of art ever produced furnished more exalted ideas of one man's genius and skill than the unceasing and regular motion of these gigantic engines when once they are set working!"

Just in case this giant should ever suffer temporary engine failure and need to rely on the forces of nature, Brunel rigged her with six towering masts to carry a colossal expanse of sail; and in the very unlikely event of meeting trouble on her voyages, she would carry not two but ten mighty anchors weighing five tons apiece.

For interior furnishings and decorations, Brunel combed the world's luxury markets and installed richly carved walnut, velvet seating, arabesque paneling, elegant cut-glass mirrors, drawing rooms such as passengers never hoped to see anywhere but in fashionable hotels. She would be born of his genius and could not avoid reflecting his own ideas of beauty.

When the *Great Eastern* was completed she was a staggering achievement; she even had artificial moonlight "all around her" provided by a gas-making plant and claimed to be "the most outstandingly original scheme of all in this superb and revolutionary vessel." On November 2, 1857, the *Great Eastern* lay on the Thames water front awaiting launch the following noon.

On account of her immense size, the liner had been built broadside-on to the river, therefore she would slip gently broadside into the water. It would be quite a simple operation.

Her great keel had been constructed across two vast cradles, each around 18 feet square, which she would take with her into mid-river. To overcome any unexpected hitch in launching, Brunel ordered a couple of powerful hydraulic rams, capable of lending a 1,000-ton pressure against her hull; and, to halt her progress once she started moving into the river, there was a series of heavy chains that would hold her back and still let her go carefully, gracefully on her way.

Londoners braved a spell of inclement weather, with

a hint of snow, and converged on the water front to witness the breathtaking event; the future Duchess of Newcastle was to perform the christening ceremony. The guests took their places on the grandstand built for the occasion, and from the shipyard came the army of men who had labored so long to complete the *Great Eastern*. Everybody had been invited as Brunel's guests; but not everybody attended. One man—a master ship-wright, seldom seen during construction, for his time had been concentrated on fashioning the double hull— was missing. Nobody knew where he could be located; maybe, the shipyard boss hinted, he had quit work and gone seeking alcoholic drink; he would show up soon enough tomorrow to draw his wages. . . .

The hands of the shipyard clock moved slowly, the waters of the river lapped gently around the launching cradles; and, from some place below the towering hull spectators heard the hollow thud of hammer blows. It was an annoying sound. But it was drowned when the assembled multitude of socialites and workmen cheered themselves hoarse as the liner was christened. Her launching gear was set in motion, drums took the strain of the heavy chains, and the ship was away.

She moved a couple of feet, a yard, then those chains brought up taut, sagged, tautened again, fell limp into the river. Slowly, the *Great Eastern* slewed around, her forepart moved exactly three and a half feet, her stern shifted seven feet; then it became obvious, her cradles, not moving in time together, had jammed, holding the ship at an awkward angle.

Experts went into hasty conference, inspected the

launching gear, shook their heads in dismay. The only thing to do, they decided, was wait until high water. A dismal silence wrapped itself around the scene . . . a silence broken unexpectedly by the thud of hammer blows from some place near the midships keel.

Lunchtime came and passed; the fabulous banquet became a mockery. The rising wind with its biting chill froze the throngs, who began drifting away. The hours dragged by, and then shortly before three o'clock, the launching drums were inspected again and set moving; the chains tautened, slacked, tautened once more, taking the strain. Nothing happened. Nothing, that is, until one of the chains burst its great links and fell into the river. The *Great Eastern* remained motionless. The remaining guests took a last look at her bulk and faded away into the growing darkness.

Days grew into weeks; the hydraulic rams were tried again and again, finally burst away from their moorings, fractured the launching cradles. On the evening of November 22, Brunel asked a fellow director of his company what he thought of the giant liner and her prospects. He was told that maybe the best thing Brunel could do was to bed her down permanently where she lay and open her to the public as a fun-fair.

Seamen passed her, outward bound in their ships, looked across the river and shook their heads. They said she would still be there next year and the years after. It looked, they told each other, as if the *Great Eastern* would stay there forever. The more superstitious seamen claimed she had a sinister streak and it would be an evil day when she sailed, if she ever did.

On November 28, Brunel tried once again, using new drums, but they too burst apart. However, while they worked they managed to shift the liner four inches at her forepart, nine inches at her stern. Then she halted and lay undisturbed through December, over Christmas and into the first week of January. With every means available, a fresh attempt was made to get her into the river, and she moved sufficiently until almost eight feet of the Thames lapped at her starboard quarter. Then she brought up to a halt.

A combination of strong easterly winds, an early spring tide and unexpectedly heavy rains did the trick where all the ingenuity of man had failed. Toward mid-March the big ship eased away, took the wrecked cradles with her, and drifted gently into the river. She was afloat. That same evening Brunel faced his fellow directors and told them, "Gentlemen, I estimated that the cost to launch our ship would be in the region of £14,000. Instead, it has now cost our company nearly £120,000."

They offered the liner for sale to the British government, claiming that in civilian service she could be a money-spinner; in time of war nothing afloat could hope to stand up to her. But the politicians were not impressed; they said they might reconsider the matter if and when Brunel could send this great liner of his into the open seas and maintain twenty knots economical speed. Two weeks later the Great Eastern Steam Navigation folded up, having exhausted its subscribed capital, and a week later the liner was bought for £160,000 by the newly formed Great Ship Company.

It was fine and warm, September 15, 1859, when the *Great Eastern*, escorted by four river tugboats as a precautionary step, steamed downriver and into the open sea at thirteen knots. Brunel was not there to watch her go—this product of his genius. He had died. The day before his death, the *Great Eastern*'s captain complained to his chief engineer that his rest had been "rudely disturbed by constant hammering from below."

Four hours later, nearing Southampton in the teeth of a stiff breeze, her pilot reported her as "quite at ease at a time when large sailing ships nearby lay under double-reefed topsails; this magnificent ship is in every respect an excellent sea boat and I can state without any hesitation that, with sufficient sea room, she is even more easily handled and under command than any ordinary ship, either under sail or steam." Moments later the casing of one of the five tall smoke stacks exploded in a deafening roar, killing six members of the engine-room crew and wrecking the grand saloon.

Fitted out at long last, widely advertised as due to "sail for the Port of New York, June 17, 1860," the North Atlantic newcomer—her new owners had given up the idea of putting her on the Australian service—lay alongside in Southampton awaiting her passengers. She had accommodation for 800 first-class, 2,000 second-class, 1,206 third-class passengers, with a crew of 400. But when she steamed out on her maiden voyage she carried thirty-six fare-paying passengers, including two women, a couple of hardy directors of the Great Ship Company and her full crew complement. She reached New York after a totally uneventful crossing on June 28; she had made a new record of eleven days.

On her second North Atlantic crossing, with one hundred passengers aboard, she made New York, a distance of 3,093 miles under steam, in ten days, and her future looked bright indeed. She was clipping off not just hours but days, as Brunel had foretold.

Her third voyage was into Quebec, commissioned as a British government transport, and she carried 2,079 soldiers, 46 officers, 159 women, 244 children, and 40 fare-paying civilian passengers. It was a splendid triumph, and complete vindication. Something sinister about this superb liner? Just foolish talk. . . .

Back in England, though on this occasion switched from Southampton to Liverpool, the *Great Eastern* was released from government requisition and returned to normal passenger service. Her advertised sailing date attracted four hundred people ready to pay for first-class accommodation, besides a number of emigrants. She steamed out of the Mersey on a mild afternoon in fall, out to the Irish coast, and altered course so that she would pass the Fastnet Lighthouse, off Cape Clear, most southwesterly point of Ireland. With supreme disdain, she steamed serenely past the record-making Black Ball packet *Underwriter*, heading into a vicious sea. Late that night the weather broke unexpectedly, but for all that, and in the teeth of increasing headwinds, the

Great Eastern was on her way west. Then, in late afternoon, somewhere below the engine-room plating, came the dull thud of hammer blows.

Minutes later, meeting mile-long combers coming at her haphazardly and with monstrous strength, she was caught broadside and almost overturned. Her terrified passengers sought shelter behind anything that looked reasonably secure. Then, moments before an enormous sea took her in its giant grip, those muffled hammer blows were heard again. A split second later one of the 58-foot paddle wheels was torn from its mountings, her rudder stock was fractured. Four lifeboats went overboard, splintered to matchwood. Indescribable scenes of panic followed as still greater seas struck at her. The second paddle wheel came unshipped and disappeared to the sea bed. One by one, her lifeboats were torn from their falls and flung into the raging seas. Furnishings were wrenched away and strewn across wrecked saloons and cabins.

By nightfall passengers were huddled in groups, alternately praying and singing hymns. Shortly before dawn the crew mutinied, broke open the liquor storeroom and began a drunken orgy. Captain Walker mustered every available male passenger, armed as many as he had guns for, set them to patrol the stricken vessel. So it continued all day until, late in the afternoon, the 3,871-ton Cunard *Scotia*, Queenstown to New York, steamed out of the east, circled the *Great Eastern*, then continued on her way. Throughout a long, agonizing night the big liner rolled helplessly. At dawn a Nova Scotian brig appeared out of the west, changed course, came alongside and looked over the scene incredulously. It seemed to one passenger aboard the stricken liner a heaven-sent chance; he hailed the brig's captain, offered £100 for every day the Nova Scotian would stand by. The offer was refused, and immediately increased with a bid to buy brig and her freight outright so that all passengers could be transferred and taken back to an English port. But the brig, taking one more disbelieving turn around the *Great Eastern,* turned on course and sailed away.

Two days later, after unceasing work patching her up as best they could, her engineers rigged a jury rudder stock, got her propeller turning, and worked the big ship painfully back into Queenstown. It was the end; she would never again hope to become a North Atlantic record maker. She was a suicide ship, they said around the coast of Britain. . . .

She was stripped of her ornate and elegant furnishings, fitted with new boilers and a new smoke stack. Between 1865 and 1866, she helped lay a section of the first North Atlantic cable; then she returned to port and was offered for sale to the highest bidder. But nobody wanted this "much belauded pet of Brunel's constructive genius"; nobody bid for her; even port authorities around Britain petitioned the government to pass a law forbidding the laying-up of the ship in waters under their control. In the end she changed hands once again, and her new owners, conceiving the idea that here was a superb floating publicity billboard, hired the

Great Eastern to a Liverpool store, whose directors had her clifflike sides plastered with posters offering "Genuine bargains for Discerning Men and Women seeking Elegant Attire and Household Furnishings."

The experiment lasted less than one month, then she lay derelict, deserted, until 1885, when a ship breaker bought her for £16,000 and arranged to have the unwanted giant towed to his yards. And as tugboats hooked their lines to her and began hauling her on her last journey, the lone watchman left aboard ran to the rails and pleaded to be taken off immediately. He had heard the thud of hammer blows, and though he searched the ship from stem to stern, he could find no trace of human agency. The tugboat crews laughed his fears to scorn, but took him aboard and hauled away at their tow. But before they could reach the breaker's yard the helpless giant appeared to slip the towlines and then tried hard to hurl herself on the nearby coast. Only by superhuman efforts was she again taken in tow and thus brought to her journey's end. There, on the slipway, opening up the double hull above the keel amidships, breaker's men found a carpetbag of rusted tools; and alongside, the skeleton of the master shipwright who had been accidentally entombed between the hulls during the final stages of the *Great Eastern*'s construction.

10.

The Man Who Never Hurried

THE INK was barely dry on the documents that made the old house my property before local tongues wagged. The information they provided was that I had acquired not only a house but a ghost— maybe, they hinted darkly, more than one.

I wasn't alarmed, for I was born in a haunted house and from an early age have been on nodding terms with such phenomena. When I told the person from whom I bought the three-hundred-year-old place what was being said, he merely grinned.

From the first time I wore gold braid on my jacket sleeves, I began learning much more than ordinary sea-manship from the Old Man. He taught me the art of life, how to take time as it came and never jog its elbow. That was his main point; never try to cram ten minutes into two, for old Father Time always catches up with you in the end.

I shall never forget the Old Man, especially when he realized that his days were numbered. To me, the knowledge was tragic; to him it was just the inevitable, the anticipated design, and he faced it calmly.

I shall never forget that close-cropped white beard of his, and the wide-brimmed sun hat he usually wore, lifting it with the sweeping courtesy of a long-forgotten age when such men found true freedom on blue water. He belonged to the grand days of sail, and as a seaman he had no equal.

The house had been in his family for nearly five generations. He treasured every stone of it. Within the tremendously thick walls, which made it delightfully cool in summertime and retained the warmth during the winter months, he and his wife had brought up a large family; but when she died their children drifted away to the four corners of the world and forgot to keep contact with him.

He had served his apprenticeship in a four-master, invested in a coastwise schooner and carried varied freights from port to port. I suspected, though there was never proof, that he shipped contraband just for the fun of it. He lost the schooner in a wild Atlantic gale, bought himself a blunt-nosed 300-ton steam freighter but couldn't settle down to life in "an old tin kettle" and eventually, convinced that he was too old to spend any more time afloat, he disposed of it and returned to the big house, to live alone.

It proved an effort for him to settle down to shore life. He had time on his hands and little to do with it. He owned a single-barrel Savage shotgun which he tucked under one arm and occasionally walked the flatlands thereabouts, or, hauling out an ancient dinghy, stalked wild fowl. That at least was the general idea, but what he actually did was to sit in that boat and drift along gently with the tide. I doubt whether he ever fired that gun with the intention of taking life. He was as gentle as they come. Once in a while, when the parson was persuasive enough, he would put on a collar and tie and read the lessons on a Sunday morning.

With VJ day I followed the Old Man ashore, decided a living might be made out of the land and looked around for a place we could convert into a real family home. He offered us the big house and we snapped it up. It was an infinitely homelike place, tailor-made for my family's needs; and the Old Man shifted his gear into a nearby four-room cottage with lattice windows that looked straight out to sea. That cottage had a sad history, but he said it suited him. There we would find him attending to his daily chores, shuffling around the place in a pair of rope-soled shoes that always seemed half a size too large for his feet.

On one wall of our new home there was a square, hand-sculptured stone inscribed with a cross and four small shields, with the legend, "God have mercy on their souls." Whose souls we were never able to discover, though I suspect they were those of a gang of smugglers who operated from the house way back in the mid-1700's and were finally run down and slain after a bloody fight with excise men.

We moved into our new home and, tired beyond measure, went to bed that first night utterly exhausted.

We switched off the light over our beds, settled down for a blissful sleep—and presently heard footsteps outside the door. The heavy iron latch was lifted, the door eased open very slowly, the latch released. We waited, expecting one of our youngsters to appear and complain of not being able to sleep in a strange house. But nobody entered. We realized that the door had opened and closed, and the air seemed to become curiously chill. Then it was all over, and we laughed, a trifle foolishly, and tried persuading ourselves we were overtired and imagining things.

But after that first night our nocturnal visitor paid frequent, if irregular, visits, and we got to thinking that if he, or maybe she, had no objection to us then we proposed ignoring the visits as if they never happened. In time, the unseen visitor became one of the family. My wife was not exactly scared but she just did not feel easy. On one occasion, when the Old Man suggested she should speak to our visitor, she said she did not dare. She was afraid it might answer back. . . .

Yes, the old house certainly had its ghost. It seemed to prefer a spare bedroom we used as a storeroom for old furniture. It was bare—except for a handsome Chippendale wall cupboard, some five feet tall, fixed permanently in a corner. It was certainly a collector's piece. Sometime in the dim past the hand-cut key had been lost and the cupboard was therefore permanently locked. I promised myself one day to open it without damage to the heavy brass lock. The Old Man's eyes twinkled when I told him this. He said, "You do that, son. But I promise you you'll find no hidden treasure; it's empty and it's always been that way. Still, you never can tell. . . ."

With the parson and a couple of the Old Man's cronies, we were sitting around a blazing log fire by candlelight one evening. That day a wild wind had blown shrieking through tall trees, whose long, spindly branches swayed before the wintry onslaught. Upstairs, a heavy oak door creaked on its iron hinges, then banged itself shut. We preferred the candlelight to electricity, and it seemed the more fitting, as we had returned home after laying the Old Man to his last long sleep under tall elms in pale December sunlight, with the wind moaning through the wild rushes and rank sea grass before it veered offshore, ruffling the tops of angry combers.

Now we were gathered in the long, cozy room, talking quietly of our old friend. It was on just such a winter night, he had told us shortly after he moved into the little cottage, when ghosts are in season from Christmas until graves yawn on Twelfth Night and, as he put it, "swallow the walking dead," that a good-looking young seaman sailed for foreign parts and left behind him one of the comeliest girls a man ever set eyes on. They had planned to wed when he returned from that voyage, and as the girl had neither kith nor kin he left her in the care of his widowed mother in the little cottage. She was radiantly happy, that girl.

But weeks stretched into months; and then came word that his ship and all aboard had been lost, homeward-bound in a North Atlantic storm. It seemed nothing could ever pacify her in her grief.

The Old Man told us that she spent hours every day wandering the nearby cliffs, peering out to sea, praying that some miracle might bring him back. Eventually, the Old Man said, overcome by grief, the girl offered her soul to the devil if he would only grant her wish. And so, one day, her lover returned.

A long period of storm and gale had swept the coastline and the seas had battered at the cliffs until a thin spume enveloped the little cottage and left rime on the latticed windows. The girl lay in bed, sleepless. She was roused by hearing her name called above the fury of the wind; she listened, and her name was called a second time.

She drew a gown around her shoulders, crossed to the window, opened it and looked out into the wild night, but could see nobody. Then, as a watery moon parted the heavy clouds, she made out the figure of her lover. He was in tattered clothing, seaweed draped about his shoulders, and blood came from a deep wound in his forehead.

She sped down the narrow stairway, threw open the cottage door, welcomed him into the warmth; she did not stop to wonder that he had returned from the dead, or that by a miracle he was the only survivor from his wrecked ship. She knew only he had come at last.

She called to her mother, and while the girl fed fresh kindling to the dying fire the older woman prepared a pot of coffee; and then the girl's lover crossed the room,

138

took her by the hand and led her out to the shore where lay a battered boat. They climbed in and disappeared out to sea. . . .

This, then, was the story of the little cottage; but there is a footnote. Some weeks before the girl's adopted mother died, the Old Man bought the cottage from her, and was given a seaman's St. Christopher medallion. That medallion had been given by the girl to her lover the day before he sailed on his last voyage . . . and it was found inside the cottage the night he returned from the dead. I held the medallion in my hand and looked it over, then returned it to the Old Man without speaking. Words seemed unnecessary. I accepted the story he told, though other local folk dismissed it as a romantic legend. But from that story, and from my evergreen memories of the Old Man, this book really had its beginning.

I journeyed far and wide seeking material which I could incorporate in this record of the supernatural at sea. I met people in all walks of life who told me strange stories. I collected stories from Iceland and the Indian Ocean, from the Florida Keys to California, from the Caribbean to the China Seas. I learned of a phantom ship which still haunts the Gulf of St. Lawrence and whose origin was a tall ship wrecked near Prince Edward Island during the last century. In San Francisco, I heard tell of the Cape Horner *Tennessee*, a gold-rush clipper, which, under full canvas, every so often nears the Golden Gate and disappears in a blue-gray haze.

Along the coastline of Europe I picked up a dozen

different stories of phantoms, such as the Belgian ship *Concordia* which appears only immediately before bad weather in the English Channel. I heard a story in La Plata, of a wealthy Latin-American who saw a phantom ship with his only daughter aboard, thirteen days before the ship was reported lost. I found a strange parallel, on the Indian coast, to the Bret Harte story of children who climbed aboard a derelict hulk moored on the water front, and the vessel broke adrift and was carried out to sea; at times it returns to the scene of the tragedy, manned by a crew of children.

I heard of ghost ships said to haunt the Hudson River and its approaches; another, the phantom of a French schooner, off the Newfoundland coast; and yet another, a French privateer, lost in the mid-1800's off Nova Scotia. Maine, Rhode Island, Salem, a dozen other places along the Atlantic seaboard, provide stories of the supernatural as well as the coastlines of Scandinavia, Africa and Australia. I met officers and men of the British Navy, who had served tours of duty in and around the Yangtze River, ready to vouch for the authenticity of a story heard around the China Seas these past three hundred years—the story of a lovely Chinese girl abducted by Portuguese pirates and never seen alive again. It is still claimed that the phantom ship, with the ghost of the girl aboard crying for assistance, is seen under full sail.

Returning to the Old Man, I want to add a footnote to my account of the old house which was our home until the fall of 1949, when naval duties forced me to sell the place with deep regret. It was as if we were saying a last good-by to an old friend, for every member of my family hated to leave.

The day before we moved out, my wife and I and a hired man went from top to bottom cleaning up so that everything would be left shipshape. Next morning, in the company of our local policeman, with whom I left the keys for the new occupants, I made a room-to-room inspection. Our footsteps sounded hollow on the uncarpeted floors of the empty house; but, as we approached the spare room, we both stopped in our tracks, listening. We heard a sound which was not of our making—the well-remembered sound of rope-soled shoes shuffling along ahead of us.

At the door of the spare room, the heavy iron latch lifted, the door swung slowly open and closed before our astonished eyes. We walked inside—and found the doors of that old corner cupboard wide open. I am convinced that the Old Man wanted to prove to me before I said farewell that the cupboard *was* empty . . . the only unusual thing about it was that the doors gave access to a winding iron stairway which, in turn, opened out into two compartments. The first led to a pathway down to the foreshore, along which, it was known for years, the smugglers of two centuries ago hauled their illicit cargoes to the big house. And the other compartment—originally, I discovered, a priest's hideout—contained bleached human bones, a tarnished sword, and a

141

faded Bible inscribed "To Elizabeth, of most happy memory."

The philosophy of the Old Man was so right; why waste time hurrying? The Man-with-the-Scythe catches up with everybody in the end.

II.

Incident in the Indian Ocean

As a living paradox, there could be no equal to the skipper of the tall, elegant three-masted bark moored on the water front one cold, bleak morning of 1899.

Between voyages, he spent his time like other folk, going about his daily business. He was an ordinary, middle-aged, unimposing man, with lean face and steady blue eyes expressing not the least hint of emotion, a type one sees often on the streets.

But afloat he conflicted with every conceivable notion of what was reasonable or possible; once aboard his ship, he had the cut of a legendary figure, able to achieve what is beyond the strength of ordinary mortals. Slight of build, he wore a short, graying beard that gave him the appearance of a buccaneer. One could imagine he kept a flintlock in his cabin and used it to blast strangers off his ship or repel raiders; he might well have been equally at home in a Viking longboat or on the quarter-deck of a modern cruiser. Nothing ever convinced him of the existence of haunted ships, though he would freely admit the possibility of haunted houses, spectral shapes lurking in dim corners ashore; nothing, that is, until this voyage to Indian ports.

He would argue that, with all the written wealth of so-called evidence of the supernatural ashore, there were no concrete instances of phantom ships or ghosts that plagued ships. He claimed that every such instance had a rational explanation. He regarded seamen as among the world's most superstitious mortals, with the inborn belief that all misfortune was attributable to unwelcome parsons, black cats, or female passengers. As for the *Flying Dutchman*, he dismissed the legend as a poor literary effort.

No one with an expert eye for ships would have said that this three-master of his, which he had commanded for upward of fifteen years, was a speedster, yet in her time she made some fine runs, notably London-Calcutta in eighty-one days. For a while she went trooping, but when de Lesseps put the finishing touches to his magnificent canal, and steam-driven ships seemed to be pushing tall sailing vessels off the world's ocean routes, her owners tried her on the long haul to Australian ports, where she produced reasonable dividends, then they returned her to the Indian ports service to end her days usefully. At her masthead she wore the house flag of one of the oldest companies in the business. Square-rigged on all but her mizzen, which was fore-and-aft rigged, she was a picture-book ship; and when she took the bit between her teeth every so often, she went like a Kentucky Derby winner.

They eased her from her water-front moorings in the London River that cold mid-winter morning of 1899, let her thread her own leisurely passage among a varied collection of ships and, as always when passing steamships with their noisy thump-thump of triple-expansion engines, like a woman turning up her nose at a displeasing odor, she lifted her stem and went her way.

She swung downriver, past the Old Stairs of Wapping, past Limehouse Reach with its bow-windowed water-front houses, past the Isle of Dogs, so named because an English king once maintained royal kennels thereabouts. Then she took the wide sweep off Blackwall Reach where, not so many years before, gibbets bore the bodies of river pirates hanging in creaking chains. To her, to her captain, all this was home; and it would be many months before she returned. She was bidding farewell to all these well-known landmarks, as she had so often done in the past.

The wintry sunlight glinted momentarily on her gleaming brasswork and moved fleeting across her black-and-white deckhouses; then she was gone in the haze. She dropped her hook at sundown, a ponderous lump of metal with a vast stock and even vaster rings on the purchase of the cathead, and came to rest swinging leisurely on the tide as her crew set to shaking down. Sixty-eight officers and seamen, with four apprentices, were her tally, but now she was short four ordinary seamen. Meantime, the remainder stowed their sea chests and ditty bags, each man jealous of his own spike, his own set of sailmaking needles, great three-sided affairs with points well worn, and his own horn of grease.

Stowing their gear, they talked together, a bunch of broad-chested men with the hearts of children; resourceful men they were, good to sail with in times of stress or emergency but, as their skipper knew, bitten deep with senseless superstition. In the main, though they would be the last to admit it, they were a deeply religious crowd.

Her four apprentices, all from good homes, had been indentured by their parents to the owners, and a bond paid against their deserting the ship before completing their apprenticeship; that bond, a substantial amount, wasn't easy to find when a boy was one of a large family. After four years of hard work and theoretical examinations had been passed, the boy qualified as second mate, usually when he was about eighteen. Thereafter he had the chance of a master's deep-sea ticket before he reached the ripe old age of twenty-five. So it was nothing unusual for an eighteen-year-old second mate to rule the toughest bunch of seamen anywhere afloat.

By sunset, the passengers filed aboard and the decks were crowded with seasoned planters and merchants returning from a spell in England rubbing shoulders with side-whiskered young men making their first voyage to India. Among them went the second mate, cursing the world in general as he superintended stowage of passengers' belongings in the main hatch. Alongside, crimps' rowboats sold hard liquor to the crew; and from a chandler's longboat came stores, including live

146

poultry to be housed in coops on the poop deck, and a score of live sheep that would be accommodated in quarters staked off near the mainmast.

An hour later, with some semblance of order on deck, a rowboat put out from the water front and spilled its sorry-looking passengers aboard—four listless seamen rounded up at the last moment by a crimp to whom they owed debts; he was glad to have them off his hands, money or no money. The first mate looked them over, muttering unprintable comments well known to men of the sea.

The night hours slipped by and, by dawn, her blue peter aloft, she was ready to go. A pale sun climbed into the eastern sky as her capstan was manned; the pilot took a last look around her decks, nodded to the skipper, and her anchor cable came slowly aboard. She was on her way, feeling the bite of a freshening wind in her sails. Her house flag dipped as she rounded Barking Creek and headed for the open sea. Later she rolled through the short Channel seas, heading into the west. In his cabin the skipper prepared to sign on the four last-minute ordinary seamen; at his side stood the senior apprentice, due at the conclusion of this voyage to become second mate.

The skipper had carried out this necessary bit of paperwork so many times in the past, he could have recited the ship's articles from memory. But it had to be done. The second mate pushed open the door. The four ordinary seamen filed in and the captain looked them over. A poor lot, he decided, but maybe they

147

could be licked into shape; he took a seat at his desk and intoned the words:

> . . . hereby engaged to serve as sailors and agree to work aboard the said ship in the several capacities set against our names on voyage from London to Bombay. And we do agree to conduct ourselves in an orderly, honest and sober manner, and to be at all times diligent in our respective duties, and to be obedient to the lawful commands of the said Master, or of any persons who shall succeed him, and of any and all superior officers, in everything relating to the said ship and the stores and cargo thereof, whether on board, in boats or on shore; in consideration of which services to be duly performed it is also stipulated that advances on account and allotment of part of wages shall be made as specified against the names of the respective seamen in the columns provided for that purpose. . . .

The captain's voice droned on to the end; then he sighed, waited as the four men scrawled signatures to the document, and dismissed them. From now on they would be the mates' headaches. To the senior apprentice he said:

"That's how we do it, my son. Never forget, a seaman has his rights equally with those of his master. You get along to the galley and find some hot coffee." He shivered. It was a bleak, inhospitable day.

The apprentice had taken a seat on an upturned bucket in a dark corner of the cook's domain when the four newly signed seamen ambled in, seeking hot coffee also. Craggy-jawed character that he was, the cook, in the light of his galley fire, appeared a bare-chested mountain of a man whose steel-blue eyes plainly showed that he would just as soon fling a cleaver at unwelcome visitors like these as dish out their chow. Long ago, on the Indian run, the cook had slept on deck one stifling night and been moonstruck, which, it was said, had twisted his mouth and given him a cruel expression. Actually, he was almost as mild-mannered as the skipper, but his fearsome-looking face paid dividends.

He shoved four cans of coffee across the top of his galley stove, looked across at the senior apprentice and deliberately winked an eye; then he addressed himself to his four visitors.

"Ain't seen anything the likes of you since I come up screamin' from a nightmare when I was a kid." He paused, allowing his preamble to sink in, and continued: "Tired o' living, are you? You don't bear no resemblance to seamen, but who cares? We ain't callin' no place till Bombay, so you got to go through with it." He contrived a twisted leer, lowered his voice as if about to impart a fearful warning. "I reckon it won't be long before th' Old Man breaks your perishin' 'earts; that is, if he don't bust your heads in first. Why else d'you think he got the name Haunted Cap'n?"

"I'll tell you," he said, "and what I'm tellin' you is truth. We was beatin' north at the time, along the Bay o' Bengal, and the Old Man a-drivin' her like no man in his senses ought. He gets the notion the helmsman ain't on his mark, so he grabs a belayin' pin, meanin' to put the fear o' God into the poor devil, when along comes an ugly sea, climbs the weather rail, takes the skipper's legs from under him. As he goes down, the helmsman does the same, only with a busted skull.

"We buried 'im that same day. We dassn't take a peek at the Old Man as he reads the committal service, an' when it's over somebody calls him the Haunted Cap'n, an' the name sticks. 'Cause why, you ask? 'Cause we know the ghost of the dead helmsman'll come back aboard soon as it's decent. That same night, in dirt, the watch was doin' their best to shorten sail which is comin' adrift from the bolt ropes, when one of 'em lets out a yell which can be heard at Cape Stiff, sayin' as how he's seen a ghost. Then he passes out an' would've fell clear to the deck if a mate hadn't grabbed him.

"They get him down on deck, carry him to the skipper's cabin. The Old Man looks him over an' swigs a tot o' rum between the poor devil's teeth. When he come to, the seaman says he's seen a ghost. 'Yes,' says th' Old Man, skeptical, but always ready to humor a loony, 'an' what did this here ghost look like, tell me that?' 'Why, it was th' helmsman!' cries the seaman, half out of his wits. 'It comes edgin' toward me in the yards, looks me clear in the eye, but it ain't got no eyes —only empty sockets!' Then he gets up, bolts for the door, yellin' 'You murdered him! Now it's come back to haunt you and the ship!'

"That's all he got to say before he was out on deck and over the weather rail, an' we never saw him again." The cook drew a breath that whistled between his teeth. "You fellers take my tip. Don't never cross paths with the Old Man, not unless you ain't got no more interest in life."

The four men shuffled out of the galley, muttering; it was a story the cook had told a dozen times before to newcomers he disliked on sight. It was always the same, highlighting the skipper as a fiend in captain's rig.

And right now, that same "human fiend" was welcoming into his cabin a favored passenger, an elderly planter making his last voyage to India. The skipper poured a generous measure of whisky for his guest, helped himself to a glass of neat unsweetened lime juice, for he had been a strict teetotaler since he first went to sea. They toasted each other. Then the guest asked whether the cook still told that old fantastic yarn of his, and how did it feel to be a haunted captain? The skipper grinned.

"There was one occasion," he said, "when I was nearly convinced we had a real ghost aboard. We were homeward bound from Melbourne at the time and made good running as far as Cape Town, when the weather broke and we were forced to heave-to. We lay waiting the wind to ease and, as it did, the entire ship seemed curiously quiet. Then a seaman came running, scared out of his wits, and said he had heard a 'fearful sound' in the fo'c'sle, like a dying man would make—the death rattle. It seemed two or three other hands had heard it, so I decided the only thing to do was organize a search party and scour the ship from stem to stern, if only to prevent panic.

151

"With the second mate, I took charge of one party, with the first and third mate starting from stern; we proceeded in the direction of the fo'c'sle and there, to our astonishment and, I suspect, to the men's utter dismay, we saw a white-clad figure, its arms raised to the skies, with long, fair hair down to its shoulders. It uttered a fearful cry, and the men in our party fell to their knees, covered their eyes or prayed as if the last day was upon them and they were coming up for judgment. It was a tense moment. And then the second mate stepped forward and took that 'ghost' in his arms and carried it to my cabin. It was one of our passengers, a young woman suffering from some mental disturbance. She recovered soon enough. We had no more hauntings after that, and this ship never will. Take my word on it."

"But that death rattle?" the skipper's guest asked.

"Quite simple," said the skipper. "Just a loose guy rope rattling in the wind against the fo'c'sle door. No sir, in thirty-odd years I've spent at sea I've yet to find anything genuine in any of the stories of the supernatural."

"You may live to learn," said his visitor.

With a favorable following wind, in good weather and calm seas, the bark pushed ahead and made the running in elegant style. She rounded the Cape of Good Hope, stuck her forefoot into cross-seas and headed into the 4,600-mile run to Bombay. Six days later the course was set for the final leg of her voyage, due northeast. But then the glass fell rapidly and within a matter of hours the wind reached full gale force with monstrous seas cracking over the weather rail.

Poultry coops were stove in and washed adrift; cabins were flooded as cataracts of water poured over luckless passengers. The galley was cleared by a mountain of water and reduced to chaos. Sails were torn adrift from gaskets and hung in shreds. On the orders of the captain, oil bags were hauled out of the main hatch, hung out to windward and punctured so that their contents would smooth the water. For a whole day the crew fought like demons to save themselves and the ship. With a lull in the gale fury, they cleaned up much of the wreckage, got one of the galley stoves going, and the cook prepared a meal. Then it blew again, though now with less venom.

In the middle watch, a day later, gripping the wheel spokes until the knuckles of both hands showed white, the helmsman gulped his coffee and spoke grimly.

"You seen more'n your share of real dirt these last few days, I reckon? God knows, we'd never have come through without the Old Man. An' did you see the face on him?"

"Who? The captain?"

"For Gawd's sake, you didn't see it? Th' first mate? I tell ya, there was th' mark on him!"

"The mark?"

"Didn't I say it? Th' mark of a man lookin' death in th' eyes. Dead scared. And that goes for the second mate too. Yeller-bellied, them two. Look. . . ." The helmsman lowered his voice. "Me, I've sailed in this ship the las' five trips, but no more. We make Bombay—if we ever make it, that is—an' I figure I'll go ashore, buy me a bellyful o' liquor an' forget to come back aboard.

"There's better mates, mebbe better ships than this. I'll sign aboard somethin' that ain't got a couple o' walkin' corpses on her poop callin' themselves mates. These last few days o' dirt scared th' guts outa both of 'em. There's only the Old Man left doin' the work of two mates, an' that don't get ships to port, does it? Like a man sleepwalkin', the Old Man was, when he tells me, beginnin' of this watch, 'Nor'east, helmsman, an' keep 'er steady there.' With that he walked away, out on his feet. It ain't human. That's why I'm gettin' out, see?"

The senior apprentice contrived a grin: "Bide your time," he counseled. "You're tired, like the rest of us. Once we tie up in Bombay you'll feel different. Why, you'll—" He stopped in the middle of the sentence.

"I'll do what?" the helmsman asked.

The apprentice nudged his elbow. "Pipe down. We've a visitor—"

Without so much as by-your-leave, a tall, barrel-chested man pushed past the astonished helmsman and peered into the compass; the binnacle light emphasized in strong relief the ugly weal of a wound that curved across one temple, bisected the cheek, ended just below the grim-set lips. "Steer nor'-nor'east."

The helmsman was plainly startled by the abrupt order: "Beggin' your pardon, but I ain't takin' no course th' Old Man didn't give me. Nor'east, he said."

The stranger spoke again, this time with an urgent note in his voice: "I said to take the ship nor'-nor'east, man, and look lively, for every moment counts!" Then he was gone.

"For God's sake," implored the puzzled helmsman, "what am I to do? Look, you just step out on th' poop an' tell th' second mate I been ordered to change course. I ain't changin' course without th' Old Man's say-so; him or the second mate's."

As puzzled as the senior apprentice, the second mate asked the helmsman, "Who was this man?"

"Ain't no idea, sir. He come in here, ordered me twice to change course, then walked out. So do I take 'er nor'-nor'east or don't I?"

"Best ask the Old Man," suggested the apprentice.

"He's sleeping," objected the second mate, "so he wouldn't thank me for rousing him. You said nor'-nor'east, helmsman—that's what you were told?" The helmsman nodded in reply. The second mate passed a hand across his eyes, then looked at the compass: "All right, man—plenty of searoom around these parts. Take her nor'-nor'east like you were told." And the bark swung slowly on her fresh course. . . .

The skipper was just awakening from his first real sleep in a week when excited shouting on deck brought him tumbling to his feet. A pale dawn had broken, splitting the heavy skies with shafts of light, and in that light four lifeboats were coming alongside, oars shipped by men reaching the limit of human endurance. They were helped aboard and their spokesman moved wearily across to the captain.

"Our ship took fire," he explained, like a man waking from a hideous nightmare. "We did our best to quench the flames, but the wind fanned them and there wasn't a chance. She burned down to her water line, then went down. You showed up just in time, for we couldn't have lasted another hour."

"Your captain here?"

"No, sir. He was killed as we lowered our boats. The burning mainmast split two-thirds of its length and he was struck across the head and knocked overboard. We searched, but failed to find any trace of him. He was our only fatality. There are some of us with minor wounds, but nothing serious."

They were taken below to be tended. Shortly after dawn the lookout called: "Object off th' port bow, sir!" It was the lifeless body of a man; a tall, barrel-chested man whose face was disfigured by a wound running from the left temple to the pain-twisted mouth, set firm in death. . . .

This, then, is the story that was told me during Christmas, 1959; the story of a ghost captain who came aboard the elegant three-master and changed her course so that his officers and crew might be spared. I have, with permission, filled in just a few gaps in the story. Who was my storyteller? A retired naval commander, a man who chose the sea straight from school at the age

156

of fourteen. He was the senior apprentice who attended the skipper while he read ship's articles to the four tardy seamen, and who sat enjoying himself in the galley while the cook spun his crazy yarn. He was, also, the youngster who was with the helmsman when the phantom captain came aboard and altered ship's course.

I have purposely omitted names of both ships out of consideration for the feelings of any living relatives of the officers and men concerned. But in every other respect the story is true and set down as faithfully as it was told to me. My storyteller added this comment: "There will be many people ready to dismiss and disbelieve such a story, but I vouch for its complete accuracy. The sea is full of strange happenings, and miracles *do* happen at times."

And the captain of that elegant three-master? In Bombay he attended to all his ship's affairs, returned aboard and watched her homeward freight stowed safely away. He handed her over to the Bombay pilot, then went down to his cabin and, for the first time since the shipwrecked crew were saved, indulged in some hard thinking. He was convinced at last of the supernatural at sea.

12.

The Falkenberg Phantom—
Again

AMONG the rare reference books I have gathered in the last few years, one work never fails to give me hours of entertaining reading, preferably on winter evenings before an open log fire while the wind moans outside and the owl hoots in the barn nearby.

The book is *Legends and Superstitions of the Sea and Sailors in All Lands and at All Times*, a typical nineteenth-century title for a formidable volume compiled by Lieutenant Fletcher S. Bassett, U.S. Navy, published in 1885. It must have taken the author many years afloat and ashore collecting stories and legends, checking and cross-checking facts since the time of the Phoenician seafarers. His references in themselves would make a sizable second volume. A fine piece of work, this, and worthy of top-shelf rating in any armchair sailor's home where quality is appreciated.

On one point the author made I raise objection. He equates the legend of Falkenberg, previously mentioned in my book, with that of the *Wandering Jew,* and writes:

> This story of Falkenberg, we must remember, was located in the North Sea, hence is probably older than all others of its kind. Perhaps here, also, the early conflict between Christianity and German Paganism may have had its effect, as Conway shows it did in perpetuating the legend of the Jew . . . but the advent of steam *forever* banished the shadow and legend of Falkenberg from nautical minds and at long last terminated the eternal punishment of this sea-wanderer. The legend was *quite* destroyed when ships were able to move against wind and tide. But the spectral Falkenberg had his revenge, for he seems to have taken with him into obscurity the traditional sailor, now almost as much a memory as the Phantom Ship of the North Sea and others elsewhere.

I challenge the claim that modern ships drove spectral shapes and supernatural manifestations from the world's ocean highways, and for this I shall no doubt be scorned by many of my readers. But in self-defense, I plead I am a seafaring man first, a writer second; so I cannot accept Bassett's thesis, nor for that matter will many others whose business takes them afloat in deep waters. One such man is third officer of a modern ocean-going tanker with a story to tell which, I think, bears out my claim that Falkenberg was not banished when steam-driven ships appeared; far from it.

My own experience of life on a deep-sea tanker is limited to a period shortly before World War II when I served a spell in such a ship operating between Curaçao and European ports. She was an antiquated freighter, and it was in her that I became acquainted with what was then called "tankeritis." Specialists eventually put a scientific name to this occupational ailment, just as they did in World War II with battle fatigue and shell-shock.

It is not easy for a visitor of even twenty-five years back to forget Curaçao; it struck me, I recall, as a macabre place to live and work in. We tied up at a wharf some distance from the main oil refineries, for the town itself was located at the extremity of a wide gulf which, at that time, was not quite deep enough to accommodate ocean-going ships. A fleet of lighters brought the low-flashpoint freight out to us at the wharf.

Curaçao produced around ten million tons of oil every year and boasted the world's largest refineries. All I can vouch for is that the fumes and smoke blackened the landscape for miles around and transformed what were once flourishing coconut, mango and banana plantations into mockeries of man's endeavor to make things grow. Somehow, though, around four thousand white and colored folk contrived to live and flourish there. The only available transport was a haphazard bus service between those refineries and the collection of smart terra-cotta bungalows, brightly painted cafés and enticing little stores which relieved the grim appearance of the place but must have cost a lot in upkeep against those encroaching oil fumes.

An engineer friend of mine, in charge of one refinery where crude oil was passed through giant condensers to emerge, after being pumped at high pressure into furnaces heated to around 310°C., as motor-spirit, kerosene and gas-oil, showed me around the place. We paused beside an overseer, motionless in front of a mass of switch gear; only his eyes seemed to be moving, nothing else. He and his relief, I was told, maintained round-the-clock watch, just in case a feed pipe fractured. This happened now and then, and when it did, unless the overseer moved with lightning speed, there could have been a cataclysmic disaster and Curaçao maybe wiped off the map. It was not apparent on the surface, but most folk in Curaçao had an acquaintance with tensed nerves, and who could blame them?

Aboard a foreign tanker moored ahead of my own ship, men were chipping rust from the sides of empty tanks. Wind sails were rigged to take fumes away—and one of those chipping hammers dropped and caused a small spark, and blue flames danced all around that ship while longshoremen and seamen held their breath and watched until the danger was over.

We pulled out two days later, with capacity freight of around 12,000 tons of high explosive under our decks and were on our way toward Europe. She took it green, like a submarine, for a fully laden tanker always made the going half-seas under. Three days after leaving that wharf we skirted the eye of a hurricane and, when we cleared the area on the sixth day, after a period when every man jack aboard wondered if he would see another dawn, a couple of seamen came to blows after a minor argument. It was over in a flash. One of them fell heavily, struck his skull on a stanchion and died; that same afternoon the other man slit his wrists open. They had been good friends, but there it was. "Tankeritis." Nerves, if you prefer—nerves stretched taut in men who spent their working life aboard a ship whose accommodation was confined and which, in fact, was nothing more than a floating volcano.

A year later, the captain's steward took in his supper one night, and shortly before midnight the second mate went along to report as watches changed. But the skipper was not there, and subsequent investigation indicated that between ten o'clock and midnight he must have walked out of his cabin and off his ship, in mid-ocean. He had been due to retire at the end of that voyage; but nerves beat him in the end.

I have mentioned these prewar experiences of mine for one purpose; I want to emphasize the fact that tanker life in those days and in that type of ship cannot be compared with life in the big modern ships of today; and that means that tankermen suffer no more from nerves nowadays than do crews of other big blue-water freighters.

The modern tanker is basically designed to ensure stability while carrying heavy freight; to prevent excessive surging of the freight when the ship rolls and pitches, its free surface is reduced by thwart-ship bulkheads. These divide the entire freight space into about ten main tanks subdivided by fore-and-aft longitudinal bulkheads to make up thirty or more separate oil-tight compartments, with cofferdams that isolate the liquid freight fore and aft from the engine room and store-rooms. In my day, we had none of these precautions. And, so far as crew accommodation is concerned, I reckon we would have disbelieved it possible.

The average 12,000-ton tanker these days has a crew of around forty-five; a 32,000-tonner anything between fifty-six and sixty-three, divided into deck, engine and catering departments; with captain, three or four navigating officers, radio officer, half a dozen engineer officers, electrician, navigating and engineer apprentices, chief steward, chief cook, bosun, carpenter, engine-room storekeeper and donkeyman, able seamen, firemen, stewards.

Every member of a modern tanker crew has his own cabin and in most companies captains' and chief engineers' wives accompany their husbands; on short-haul or coastwise trades, wives of other officers go along, too. Shore leave is generous, equipment aboard is as good as any home ashore . . . a long, long way from the time when ships were shoved through the seas with protesting triple-expansion engines and had to be rigged with masts and sails in case those engines quit. That was not so many years ago, either.

Where does this preamble lead? To a story told me by the third officer of the 12,000-ton motorship *British Empress*, a fine, up-to-the-minute tanker any man would be glad to serve in. And this story, so far as I am concerned, bears me out in my protest to Fletcher Bassett's claim that steam put an end to the Falkenberg legend. I can do no better than quote the actual story of this third officer as he set it down for me:

My eyesight is first-class, so is that of the deck officer, the captain and helmsman concerned; and the same applies to the pilot we had with us. This point I had best make quite clear before proceeding further, and for obvious reasons.

At the latter end of winter, 1958, I was on the short haul coastwise run aboard the *British Empress*, with oil freights mainly from Grangemouth, Scotland, and the Isle of Grain, England, to Scandinavian countries, our chief port of call being Nyköping, Sweden, in the Baltic. We were in pilotage waters, outward bound at the time, and I took over watch on the bridge at 20:00 hours, relieving First Officer T. H. Wall, a native of Inverkeithing, Fifeshire, a tough, unimaginative seaman and one of the very best.

It was a dark night, but quite clear with a moderate to a slight breeze from astern. The radar was on and working well on all ranges, though we were using only the three- and twelve-mile limits. This was not strictly necessary in view of the exceptional visibility, but we had been advised by Captain G. F. Davies, whose home is in Cheshire, England, to use our radar in pilotage waters since it was never certain when fog might suddenly and unexpectedly come down.

Captain Davies was of course also present on the bridge, and he is a first-class navigator, a fine man in every respect. Shortly before he handed over to me, First Officer Wall checked with me navigational matters and forthcoming alterations of course; and then he told me quite calmly that he, our pilot and Captain Davies had seen, and in fact altered course for, a ghost

164

ship which had appeared, he said, on a line of bearing of two-and-a-half to three points on our starboard bow, in the form of two yellowish lights, as of a steamship's masthead lights suddenly appearing out of fog. No side lights of the ship had been visible, nor was there any fog at that time.

Since this bearing indicated an uncomfortably close line of nearest approach our pilot ordered, so far as I can now recall, alteration of 20° to port. Had these strange lights given the appearance of a crossing vessel, or a vessel on collision course, we would, under international law, have been obliged to alter to starboard, or, had that been impossible or impracticable, would have reduced speed, stopped, or gone astern. The alteration taken was therefore a precautionary measure. The lights had disappeared, though immediately before they did, they were less than 100 yards distant from us and were fast closing.

I received this information from the First Officer with some reserve.

A few minutes after 20:00 hours we dropped our pilot and proceeded outward, to master's orders— TMO in the language of navigating officers. Then, almost immediately after the pilot left us, and with Captain Davies on the bridge nearby, I sighted two yellowish lights rather like those of a steamship coming astern out of fog on our port quarter. Here I should point out that it would be quite impossible to see the masthead lights of any vessel from an angle beyond two points abaft her beam.

Again, neither would side lights be visible under this rule, and, in fact, none was visible. The lights were around half a mile distant, very close by nautical standards, and rapidly coming up with us at around thirty knots, an excessive speed for any vessel in those waters.

I called to Captain Davies, who at once said that this could only be the ghost ship they had sighted earlier, and he focussed her in his glasses. I went to our radar, which was then working on the three-mile range, gave it fine tuning but failed completely to sight any object whatever on our port quarter within that range; even on the twelve-mile sweep there was nothing.

I took the glasses from Captain Davies and looked closely at the two lights but was unable to make anything of them, nor could I see anything like a ship or indeed anything at all but those two yellowish lights moving at speed about thirty feet above the water. Then the foremost and higher light slowly sank to the surface of the seas so that we could quite clearly see its reflection, then it sank beneath the water, or otherwise disappeared. Then the second, lower light did the same thing. It was quite inexplicable and uncanny. We knew, from our own wartime experiences hereabouts, and from stories common among officers and men on this run, there was a story of a German ship, type never stated accurately, which was said to have gone down in strange and tragic circumstances and no trace of her had ever been seen.

You may not believe the story I have told, and I could not blame you, but what I have written are the plain, unvarnished facts. My statements may be readily verified should you wish by contacting the two officers and our pilot concerned; they may, in fact, have other things to add to my own story. I have no doubt that the marine authorities in Nyköping would readily supply information with regard to this incident in their area. I would like to add that neither Captain Davies,

166

First Officer Wall, our pilot or I would like ever to sight that pair of lights again.

I contacted the officers concerned and the Nyköping authorities and satisfied myself that this incident occurred exactly as it was told to me, for the purposes of this book. I would not presume to add anything to the story, or attempt to dramatize it in any way; but I would like to make this point. From my story in Chapter 3, you may recall that Falkenberg was supposed to be able to change the shape of his spectral ship and at times to display misleading navigational lights. Well, another treasured volume in my small personal library is Thorpe's *Northern Mythology*, from which I quote this brief passage:

> For six hundred years Falkenberg has sailed his phantom ship and at times is said to change her appearance and rig; he sails to the north, the south, the east and the west, and whichever course his phantom ship takes, there, too, go two small, yellow-tinted lights which, it is said, shall accompany Falkenberg until the Last Day.

So, I submit, the gallant Lieutenant Fletcher Bassett was not strictly correct in his claim.

13.

Australian Interlude

I SUGGEST that a ship need not be an old-timer to be haunted. Take the case of the *Port Pirie*. . . .

A thousand skilled men in a dozen different trades built the *Port Pirie* in the big yards of Swan Hunter and Wigham Richardson, on the River Tyne; like the craftsmen they were, they took steel and fashioned it first into a skeleton with gaunt, bare ribs, then draped flesh around those bones. They put a great heart into this vast structure that grew with each new day, and then added veins. They built houses high up there, and installed a complicated system of electronic machinery; and when their task was completed they had produced a fine twin-screw ship, with powerful Doxford engines, with four magnificent Allen generators, with ample refrigerated space; yes, and a host of other items, large and small. Those engines, which were the very heart, were capable of 16½ knots economical speed, 17-plus in favorable conditions.

Accommodation was provided for captain, four navigating officers, ten engineers, two refrigerating engineers, chief and second electrical engineers, radio officer, a crew of seventy, and twelve first-class passengers.

The *Port Pirie* was scheduled to carry mixed freight from London or Liverpool for Adelaide, Melbourne, Sydney, Brisbane, Auckland, Wellington, Port Chalmers and Littleton; then, with a full load of meat, butter, cheese and fruit, back to London, Liverpool, sometimes Glasgow. Right around the world and back.

Gross tonnage was registered at 10,500, and those craftsmen completed their work in 1946, when she was launched. *She?* You have only to ask any one of those shipyard men just why, to get a ready answer. They would have said a ship is called "she" for obvious reasons. They will tell you the custom goes back to the ancient Greeks, who called all ships by feminine names, maybe out of deference to Athene, goddess of the sea. Since those far-off days, all ships have vitality and intelligence, like any attractive woman.

Elaborating their theme, they will remind you that a ship possesses not only vitality, intelligence and other human qualities, but a waist, stays, ties, combings, chains, pins, hooks, eyes and watches. Also a head, and a nose, eyes, shoulders and, of course, heart and veins. Then again, when in port a ship is tended by a man familiarly known to sailormen as a "ship's husband"; and any ship always looks her best when she is dressed, rigged out by men like that. So those craftsmen and the average seaman would say, that is logic for sure.

And the *Port Pirie*, as every man among her crew

169

would proclaim, hand on heart, was a lady, albeit at times a frivolous lady. She loved nothing better than a beam sea, and her roll could be as gentle as the rocking of a cradle. Then again, no matter what stevedores, or her officers, did with the freight that was loaded into her, she was, in seamen's language, "as tender as a lamb chop." For the *Port Pirie* was a well-found ship and weather did not bother her one bit. She was a beauty, a rare beauty, in a seaway and as proud as they came; a proud ship is worth serving in, too.

Jonesy, her sixth engineer, claimed she "spoke" to to him at all times, and he knew, the moment he came on watch, whether she was well or ailing. To shore folk that may sound foolish, but it is so. And when Jonesy landed the job as sixth engineer, he congratulated himself; being a man with a great love for ships and a ship's engines, it was the natural thing to do.

Now, skeptical folk might protest that the world of phantoms would not take to a ship like the *Port Pirie*, since she was only three years old at the time of this incident, and thus far too new. Ghosts could only haunt old-timers, especially old-time sailing ships which had been through checkered careers. And they would be wrong, those skeptics.

It happened in 1949, when the *Port Pirie* was alongside the Sydney water front after a fine run out from United Kingdom ports. In such times it usually falls to the unenviable lot of junior engineers to work nights in the engine room, from around the beginning of the middle watch until just before the morning watch takes

over, tackling odd jobs the senior second engineer figures need tackling. And on this night Jonesy had been
required by the senior second engineer to repack the
swing arms of the port main engine, which meant he
would work most of the time right inside the engine
crankcase. Not a particularly enjoyable space to be confined in on a night like that, for it was unbearably hot
and humid. Keeping him company would be the donkeyman, new to the job, whose work was no more
strenuous than tending the small, oil-fired Cochrane
boiler.

Jonesy and the donkeyman went on watch around
11 P.M. and even then reckoned it seemed a mighty
long while before the clock showed seven and released
them from duty.

The polished steel handrails felt unusually slippery
with a mixture of oil and moisture as they stepped below, and the engine-room atmosphere was in sharp con-
trast with what little fresh air there was on deck. It was
far too warm, too steamy, for in any ship, in port or
afloat, some steam always manages to find its way outside the steam pipes and cylinders. Tonight, the place
did not echo with the noise of thumping machinery,
and that was a blessing, Jonesy thought, though it did
seem to create a strangely quiet atmosphere. Maybe too
quiet. Only the diesel generator over on the starboard
side was working, and then merely with a soft burring
sound.

They stepped down to the engine-room plating;
right across the way was the fire room and, on a night

like this, no place for any man to work in. Away toward the stern was about the quietest place down below, an alleyway in which ran smooth columns of steel which turned around and around when the ship was at sea, without a sound. Those columns, stilled now, were the propeller shafts.

Jonesy paused and gazed around him and aloft; this was a spacious compartment, as lofty, as imposing in its way as a cathedral and nearly as silent. He wondered why deck officers took so little notice of the heart of a ship; not exactly the tactful thing to do, for without an engine room a ship is useless. The engineer makes machinery work, taking a ship across the seven seas and back; but navigating officers ignore the engine room, as a man ignores his stomach until something goes wrong. And when something goes wrong in the engine room, the deck crowd are as helpless as a man with acute dyspepsia and just about as cheerful.

He climbed into the crankcase and climbed out again. A thought had struck him. He called to the donkeyman, "Everything under control?" The donkeyman nodded. "Okay," said Jonesy, "then you nip up aloft and grab a couple of hours' sleep. I'll take care of that Cochrane job while you're away. Maybe, according whether I've got these swing arms repacked around three o'clock or thereabouts, we'll change places and you can take over until seven."

The donkeyman grinned. "Suits me, but what would the second say?"

"Plenty—if he knew, but he doesn't and won't."

The donkeyman climbed the long steel stairway and disappeared, and Jonesy went to work inside the port main engine crankcase; as he worked he could hear the generator running, a comforting sound muted by distance. For between that generator and him were the two main engines; and the boiler room, a half-enclosed compartment, was located in the engine room's port forward section, and from inside the crankcase he could hear a slightly louder sound—the sound of the feed pump as it fed water into the boiler.

He had always had his own pet label for the sound that feed pump made. He called it the "engineer's lullaby." For the piston of the pump started on its up-stroke with an insidious, sibilant *whee* that started well down the musical scale and worked its way slowly up; then, on the down stroke, the *whee* went into reverse, and each subsequent *whee* ended with an audible click as the shuttle valve moved across and set the whole thing in motion once more. Jonesy always reckoned it was second nature for an engineer to keep an ear tuned to that *whee*, because if it stopped suddenly, that was the signal the boiler was short of water. If a man ignored the cessation of that subtle sound, a boiler could blow up.

The hands of the engine-room clock moved toward twelve; from way up above on deck Jonesy heard the ship's bells as watches changed, the middle watch taking over from a bunch of weary-eyed seamen who needed sleep. And then, as near silence returned to the engine room, in the confined space of the crankcase

Jonesy's ears picked up the sound of that feed pump. Its *whee* had suddenly become erratic as it speeded up.

He quit work for a moment, assured himself it meant nothing, as the rate of pumping was automatically controlled; but when the sound became faster and threatened to trip over itself on down- and upstrokes, he knew he had better take a look at the thing.

He went to the boiler room. The feed pump was working flat out. He glanced over at the boiler gauge, and that indicated that the boiler was pretty near capacity. Jonesy thought it was cockeyed, for if the boiler was almost full, then there was no need or reason for the feed pump to work at pressure. He changed the pump from automatic to hand control, slowed it down, went back to his job and climbed inside the crankcase.

Within a minute the feed pump was working itself into a frenzy of activity, and Jonesy cursed. He climbed out again, investigated, found that the gauge still registered capacity load inside the boiler. He stopped the pump completely and went back to his job.

This time, there was barely a few seconds gone when that feed pump went mad, feeding water into the boiler like nobody's business. Yet Jonesy knew he had shut it off. Okay! If a feed pump felt that way, he reckoned he knew what ought to be done; this time, he promised himself as he climbed out from the crankcase, *this* time he would make dead certain it *did* stop. He selected a wheel key from a rack of engine-room tools.

Stripped of technical jargon, this is how a wheel key works: It is a spanner for closing valves, a steel bar forked at one end, with one end of the fork a hook, the other a cup—not unlike the two rests a fisherman places his rod in. By placing a wheel-key hook *over* a valve wheel and the cup *against* it, a valve can be closed hard down.

Jonesy used the wheel key and closed down that valve so tight, two strong men couldn't have opened it by hand. He stepped back and watched the feed pump. It had quit. He was satisfied it would not work again until he opened it with the wheel key. He went back to the crankcase, climbed inside, and was picking up a tool when that feed pump went completely haywire.

He stepped across to the pump with purposeful stride; *this* time, he decided, he would do what he ought to have done in the first place. He would test the boiler gauge for accuracy.

Just how long that gauge had been out of action Jonesy had no idea; all he knew was that it did not mean a thing. That boiler was so nearly empty that it made no difference, yet the gauge showed it almost full. Slowly, it dawned on him: Had it not been for the strange behavior of the shut-down feed pump the boiler would have exploded any moment now and would have destroyed itself, including the engine room and much of the ship herself. His brow was cold with sweat, his legs trembled; his hands were shaking, too, as he made good the fault, started up the feed pump and took the first deep breath in minutes. He reckoned he had a lot to be grateful for. Then he went back to the crankcase, climbed inside, set to work repacking the swing arms, and completed the job just as the morning watch was taking over at four o'clock. It had been a fearful night. He gathered his gear, crawled into his bunk, but sleep eluded him for a long time.

It was long past noon before Jonesy wakened, shaved and dressed and went along to the engineers' dining saloon. He nodded absent-mindedly at two senior engineers smoking their after-lunch cigarettes; they looked as if they were sitting on top of the world; he wished he felt that way. Last night's affair still puzzled him. He muttered thanks to the steward as a meal was placed before him, picked up knife and fork, paused as the second senior engineer, looking across the table at him with an air of good-humored indulgence, said: "You look like a man with a bad hangover. You been on the bottle?"

"If I had, I had plenty of reason."

"Yeah?"

Jonesy put down his knife and fork, pushed the plate away, leaned forward in his chair and gave them the story, punctuating each occasion when he had climbed out of the crankcase with an emphatic square-ended finger on the white tablecloth. He gave his two seniors the bare facts. No frills. And when he stopped speaking, he cocked an inquisitive eye on them and challenged: "None of the crowd tried pulling a fast one on me, maybe? There wasn't another wheel key down there anyway."

"So what?"

"Just an idea that struck me. It wouldn't have been particularly clever if somebody did."

176

"Don't be silly. Who'd want to?"

"I wouldn't know, and that's for sure. But the way I figure it somebody must have opened that feed-pump valve after I locked it, but who? I used the wheel key. The entire engine-room department put together couldn't open it after that. . . ."

One of his two listeners, a man who had served on the *Port Pirie* since her launching, lighted a fresh cigarette, drew on it thoughtfully. "Look, Jonesy, if that feed pump hadn't gone haywire, even after you locked it with the key, you wouldn't have finally checked the boiler gauge, wouldn't have found it wasn't working and the boiler darned near empty, and then . . ." He paused, blew a thin stream of blue smoke. "And then, before you could do anything more, the boiler, much of the engine room, maybe the ship herself, if there had been fire, could have been destroyed. Yes, you and us, too. No. None of the engine-room boys pulled a fast one. After you locked that valve down it wasn't any human agency opened it up again."

Jonesy stared. "What you're saying is . . . No, you're crazy!"

"Our first donkeyman we signed on shortly after the ship was commissioned. He was killed one night when that boiler blew up. Lack of water. The poor devil lived just long enough to mutter it wouldn't happen a second time, and died. And it hasn't happened again. I'm no believer in the supernatural, but I reckon I'm not wrong in saying he's been aboard *waiting for what happened last night.*"

177

" 'It won't happen again'?" Jonesy was talking quietly, as if to himself.

The steward entered the saloon. "Not feeling like lunch, sir? Like some coffee?"

Jonesy roused himself. "Eh? Oh, coffee? Black and strong. Strong as you can make it." But the coffee remained untouched and went cold.

I have set down this story exactly as it reached me from former sixth engineer Peter Jones. I would not presume to add any personal comment, for that would be unnecessary. I accept it as it stands; whether you will, it is not for me to forecast.

But I do submit that a ship need not be old to be haunted, even by a benevolent ghost like that of the *Port Pirie*'s first donkeyman.

Ghosts, so far as shore instances are concerned, are always accepted as fact when they are associated with old houses, places where anguish or cruelty in some form, black thoughts, blacker deeds *and* sudden death provide all the ingredients for such manifestations. But ghosts do not have to be medieval, with headless bodies and clanking chains; indeed, since I set out investigating this fascinating subject, I have had corroborated evidence given me of a haunted golf club house; a diner where a phantom automobile arrives, a spectral driver at the wheel; and a ghost-ridden garage. So who am I to doubt the story of the *Port Pirie*'s dead donkeyman?

14.

The Man on the Weather Yard

I CARRIED a letter in my pocket, a passport to one of the most fascinating visits I have made in a long time. It was written in a firm hand by a man who, I found out later, had earned the right to put his feet up luxuriously and take it easy the rest of his life.

But he was not that type. The postscript to his letter gave me a pretty good clue to his character long before we met. It went this way:

Perhaps I could add a personal story or two to your forthcoming book. They are quite true, though there will be plenty of people to doubt them; so, if you can spare time, why not stop by at my home for a couple of days or so. You will be very welcome. In case you can't, I am summarizing the stories in this letter. You have my full permission to use them just as you wish. If you decide to use them you can cut them short, or fill in any gaps you may find, put them into good English or leave them as they are; use my name, omit my name, or just drop this letter straight into your wastepaper basket and forget I ever wrote. But I've lived with these experiences for the last fifty years without ever telling them and I'd like to get them off my chest before I become a doddering old fool.

So off I set to make his acquaintance.

Scrub oak and red croton, and the long, tapering branches of an old tree, curving like a green roof, made a fitting frame for him as he waded ashore and greeted me when I stepped out of the speedboat. He was in skin-diving gear. He pulled off his flippers, grinned and introduced himself in a crisp hearty voice. Deep-chested, bronzed from head to heel, he could have been in his late forties; instead, he confessed, he was in his sixties.

He waved one arm and indicated the lapis lazuli waters of the sweeping bay, ruffled now by the slight breeze; a great crescent of blue with white-gold sand that fringed its dazzling shape. The sun flashed, splitting the horizon, and shone for a second full in our faces and touched the blues, the greens, the entire spectrum of varied color around us, like some magic wand. He piloted me up to his house and into his den, whose picture window gave an uninterrupted view of the bay, while the opposite windows framed a cluster of thatched cottages whose tall chimneys fed lazy blue smoke to the skies.

He offered me a deep armchair, and laid a couple of logs on the red embers of the fire. "Nothing like apple for real scent as it burns," he said. He smiled across at me, poured coffee from an elegant flask, told me to make myself at home while he dressed.

Framed by the window, a couple of horses, one chestnut, the other dapple gray, plodded along a rough track, sunlight glinting on their brasses; beyond them a flat, gray-blue mist obscured further view.

"Lovely sight," he said behind me. "I used to dream of this kind of thing as my days afloat neared their end." He chuckled. "They don't want elderly commanders these days. . . ."

It was lovely, that scene, one of the loveliest I ever looked upon. He stretched his long arms.

"Y' know the water was a darn sight warmer than I expected. I live a lazy life, enjoying the simple things. Did you ever stop to think about simple things—like touch and sound and smell? And the feel of soft rain on your skin and, nights, sitting in a room like this, smelling apple wood burning? That and the scent of candles freshly gutted and only the flames of a log fire lighting up the room. I like candlelight better than electricity, though my wife claims it's a strain on the eyes." He jerked his thumb toward the sweep of the bay. "Pirates used it as an anchorage, they say. That's why I took up skin-diving, just to see if they left anything of value on the sea bed. They didn't, but it's fun, and you never know. . . ."

The long afternoon wore on, and when night fell we sat before his log fire, the dancing flames outlining broad oak beams. He said, "Okay. We'll get down to business." He stretched his long legs before the fire. "But you don't have to believe a word of it."

He reached for a handsome stone jar, loaded tobacco into the bowl of a well-used bruyère pipe, lighted it, and began his story.

I reckon you've heard a dozen and more versions of the "extra hand" in ships? Yarns like that used to be told in a galley by some shaggy-faced hash-slinger who couldn't rightly tell the difference between a butcher's cleaver and a marlinespike. But the apprentices used to lap it up. I heard my first version of the "extra hand" aboard a windjammer, driving along in fair style under a stiff wind.

We were two weeks out from New York, bound for African ports, when we struck dead calm before the wind came back and blew us into Cape Town. It was my second voyage. Late one afternoon, after taking in our royals with the seas flat as a table top, the mate said we should get along to the galley and grab a meal, there would be plenty to do when the wind returned. We did so, eating our chow around the galley stove while the cook sat watching us with a jaundiced eye, as he sliced plug tobacco with the ten-inch blade of a sheath knife. It was fascinating watching that old shark as he pulled the shreds apart, rolled them into a neat plug and stuck it into one corner of his mouth. When he got the real taste on his palate he told us his version of the "extra hand."

I can't recall just how it went, but if the cook intended it as a blood-curdler it misfired. It didn't scare us one half so much as when that wind came back, a real howler which threatened to heel the old hooker over any moment. We made the Cape five days overdue, none the worse for the voyage. That was back in '08.

The following year opportunity was to come my way to tell a story that would have scared the skin off that cook. It was in 1909. I was then a second-year apprentice in the four-masted bark *Arrow*, flying the flag of the old Anglo-American Oil Company. We pulled out from New York with a capacity freight of case oil for Hong Kong, and we were going the long way, around the Cape of Good Hope, for economy reasons. Time didn't matter so long as our freight reached its destination.

We struck bad weather; midway across the South Atlantic the ship was lifting high and then taking it green and deep as if a pair of giant hands were pressing her down and meant to keep her there. Every once in a while a sea came over us with a roar. It was bad, but it looked like conditions might improve by dawn and we made the best of it. It was raining furiously, and Macdonald, the mate, was in his usual place on the poop, hunched up in oilskins and sou'wester, his eyes peeled like they always were at times like that, watching out for the unexpected, fearing the worst, hoping for the best.

Then he let out a howl: "Loose those royals and make it snappy!" And as he yelled to us the moon, which was nearing full, came out from behind heavy clouds, a great bawdy-looking orb it was and seemed to be taking a peek at us and enjoying what it saw, which we weren't. Unexpectedly, the wind fell and we settled down to a steady seven knots or so.

Now, it was my job to loose the mizzen-royal, but I never was as quick on my feet as Macdonald wanted me to be; looking back now I'm prepared to thank the Almighty I wasn't fast enough. So Macdonald yelled an uncomplimentary remark in my direction and ordered a seaman standing near me, a Finn, to get aloft, which he did. A minute later we got the deck hail from our fore- and main-royal yards that the canvas was ready for hoisting, which it was, and sheeted home safe.

I was keeping out of the mate's way, which seemed the wisest thing to do, for he never was a sweet-tempered man. I ducked around a deckhouse and watched aloft. Macdonald was watching, too, as he always did, expecting to find fault. We could see the Finn on our mizzen-royal quite clearly. He was halfway out on the weather yard but he wasn't doing anything, just still as if he had gone aloft to enjoy the view and had found it too absorbing to remember he was a seaman. Then a dark tension seemed to come down and surround the ship as if some evil force was about to be let loose. A seaman nearby muttered he reckoned it was "black magic." It scared me. There was *something* I couldn't put a name to.

Macdonald, mad as they make 'em, strode along the

184

deck and yelled, "What the blazes is that flamin' Finn doing in the mizzen-royal?"

"Why, 'e ain't doin' nothin' at all, sir," a seaman replied, grinning like a Cheshire cat; but the mate wiped that grin off his face with a back-hander that sent the seaman spinning on his heels. "So Mister Flamin' Finn reckons he's on some pleasure boat?" snorts Macdonald. "Okay, *you!*" He waits while the seaman picked himself up dazed. "Get aloft and give my compliments to that Finn and ask him if he'd be kind enough to step down here and have a word with me. Step lively, man!"

The seaman hadn't gone a couple of feet into the rigging before a regular doldrum swell, long and oily, came at the ship like silk, underrunning her, with pretty near no vestige of real air for a man to draw into his lungs. The bark was swinging drunkenly, groaning like a sick man. In the two years I had been afloat nothing like this had happened and I never felt that strange sensation that surrounded us. The air seemed electric.

Macdonald fretted and fumed and kept watching aloft, and then the seaman he had sent up yelled back for the mate to send up a couple more hands with snatch block and gantline. The mate, eyes popping out of their sockets, swore and promised trouble if this was some kind of feeble joke; but the two men went aloft with the gear and we watched them go. They edged along toward the Finn and the first man, who appeared to be holding the Finn by his arms; the three of them—and it was obvious from deck they had to use force—

were prying the Finn's fingers from their grip and into a bowline-on-the-bight in that gantline. Then, slowly, very carefully, they lowered him down to the deck.

The mate looked the Finn over; he lay silent and supine on the deck.

"What happened up there?" asked the mate.

"He were all glassy-eyed, hanging onto the jack stay like 'is fingers were froze. He's out and that's for sure."

Macdonald prodded the senseless Finn with the toe of his sea boot, as a man might prod the side of his dog, stirring it to life. But the Finn made no move; only his eyelids flickered. A seaman filled a bucket over the rail, emptied the contents over the Finn, and Macdonald flared up again. The sea water revived the unconscious man and he sat up weakly and stared around him. Then, as if he'd seen a ghost, he shivered, cowered against the mate's legs and looked up with terrified eyes.

The mate said, "I sent you aloft to loose the mizzen-royal. Why didn't you?"

"I ban try," the Finn answered. "I ban try dam' hard. . . ."

"You don't have to try, mister, you just do it!"

"I ban try . . ." The Finn's eyes were bad to look into and his lips quivered with real fear. ". . . but *he wouldn't let me!*"

I thought Macdonald was about to have convulsions, for his face darkened and the veins stood out at his temples and neck: "Who d'ye mean—'he'?"

186

"Fella with a scar under one eye," replied the Finn, and passed out again.

Macdonald's face was strained but he quickly recovered his normal cold composure and turned to the waiting seamen. "Get him into his bunk. Give him a hot drink. I'll be along."

Foolishly, maybe, I asked Macdonald if I should report the Finn to the Old Man. He turned on me. "You'll mind your own flamin' business, youngster. You come along with me." We went to the seamen's quarters where the Finn was propped up in his bunk. Macdonald asked him to describe what had happened in the yards and what this "he" might be the Finn talked about. The Finn told him. A big man, scarred under his left eye, dressed in torn oilskins with a bright yellow sou'-wester on his head. . . .

Macdonald's face, which had been black and strained with anger a moment ago, suddenly went white, death white. I noticed it but the seamen did not. He gripped my arm and hurried me along to his cabin without speaking. He closed the door once we were inside, unlocked a cabinet on the bulkhead above his bunk, took a long swig from a bottle of rum. "My God!" he muttered. "I needed that like I never needed anything." A thin trickle of sweat began on his temples and slowly ran down his drawn cheeks.

"Listen, son," he said, moments later, "I got to tell somebody or it'll drive me crazy. You ever heard tell of the 'extra hand' in a ship?" he asked me. I nodded but

187

said nothing. "Well, what I'm going to tell you happened during our previous trip in this same ship. The weather was lousy, with seas coming aboard to smash everything movable until sometimes we carried around a foot of water. Eight days out from New York it looked like we'd never make it and there wasn't any sense going along. Most of her regular canvas had gone, spares too, but I got the crew rigging temporary sails and bent them on fast as they knew how.

"I was on deck, keeping a weather eye open and alongside me were a couple of seamen to work the capstan. When everything was hoist as best as the men could, the two seamen stood by ready to lead the halyard ends to that capstan and then, without warning, a sea, bigger than any other I've seen, smashed over us and swept everything in its path. The old *Arrow* heeled over until her sticks came almost parallel with the seas. When she righted herself, slowly, so slowly I never thought she'd make it upright again, there he was, lying at my feet, twisted up and his neck broken. His eyes were open, but they had a terrible look in them—dead."

"Who?" I asked Macdonald.

"French Pete," he said. Then he lowered his voice to a whisper. "And you know something, son? French Pete was wearing worn oilskins and a tattered old yellow sou'wester. Also, French Pete had a long curved scar down one cheek he'd got in a maul in a 'Frisco waterfront saloon years back. Dead, I tell you, a full twelve months ago, and he was up there today, up on our weather yard, and wouldn't let the Finn come one step nearer him!"

Macdonald emptied the rum bottle, wiped his lips with the back of one hand and said: "Look, son, for God's sake, don't breathe a word of what I've told you among the crew. They're jumpy enough as it is. But they don't know *this* . . . apart from the Old Man and me, nobody in the ship on *this* voyage served in her on the *last*. So apart from the two of us, and now you, no man could possibly know that right here, clear of the sou'east trades and around thirty south and ten east like I figure we are today, we lost French Pete when he came down crashing from that weather yard, dead at my feet. French Pete, son, with that scar down his cheek and the torn oilskins and yellow sou'wester he wore!"

It was obvious to me it had been a great strain on my host telling that story and he had lived with it these last fifty years; maybe that does not sound very terrible to some shore folk, but I knew it had hurt him at the time and the passing years had done little to erase the deep mark it must have left on him. Presently, he arose from his armchair, placed a fresh apple-wood log on the fire, sat down again and seemed to be staring at a thin red tracery of burning soot back of the chimney piece. He stretched out his right hand for the tobacco jar; he handed it across to me. It was a beautiful piece of potter's craft. He said: "The bosun of the old *Dover Castle* made that. A collector's piece. He promised me I should have it if I managed to outlive him. . . ."

I asked him: "But what happened to Macdonald?"

"Never fully recovered; he quit the old *Arrow* next time we made New York."

"Was there any further—um—trouble?" I asked, "before you made Hong Kong with that case-oil freight?"

"No. None whatever. We sighted the Cape of Good Hope three days after French Pete came back from the grave, made our easting down at forty-eight south and bowled along in fine style until we reached Hong Kong." He stirred the blazing apple-wood log and his wife entered the room with a tray of sandwiches and two bottles of beer. She wished us good night and left.

I said: "The *Dover Castle?*"

"That was some years later, between the two World Wars, and I'd made the grade. Second officer in that ship, an intermediate liner belonging to the Union-Castle Line, running on the East and South African ports service. We had a full passenger list and mixed freight and made a fair passage until we passed Gibraltar; it looked as if the rest of the voyage would be comfortable and happy. You know how it is in a liner? Passengers corner you on and off watch and expect to be told fascinating stories of life afloat when, in fact, these days they might just as well be living in a hotel and them caring as much about life at sea as they do about life in the hotels.

"It's just the way passengers have. Not that I minded

talking with them, but the women got on a man's nerves at times. I liked talking about my days in sail, and they could have become fading memories if the bosun hadn't been there to keep memories like those alive with me. Like me, he was an old square-rigger man. We got together when we could and talked of the ships we had served in; those which were still managing to earn a living for their owners, those the movies had taken over for their screen epics, and those which had gone the way all ships go in the end, sail or steam. You know how it is when a couple of characters like the bosun and me get together to yarn over old times."

I nodded; I felt I understood just what it had meant for men of *his* type to talk with contemporaries about ships they had known or served in, though the days of sail were long before my own time. But I knew what he meant and how much those off-watch yarns with the *Dover Castle*'s bosun must have impressed him, and brought back the past as vividly as today. He passed the plate of sandwiches, chewed quietly awhile and told me the second story. . . .

I was officer of the middle watch. A lovely moonlit night it was and the end of what had been a perfect day. We stopped a few hours in Valetta Harbor, Malta, and then were on our way again, and the night promised a fine day tomorrow. The ship was silent, as liners always are when passengers have turned in to sleep off the effects of a good dinner. There I was, on the bridge, nothing to occupy my time but walk back and forward and once in a while take the usual look at the compass and check course, though that wasn't necessary, for we had a quartermaster at the wheel who figured he could have taught me, and any of the other old hands, how a ship should be handled. One of those modern bright young men, he was, and had served through World War I on a destroyer. You couldn't teach him a thing; not that I wanted to try, anyway.

It was uncomfortably hot, and I remember thinking, as I paced the bridge, what I'd give for a long cold drink with ice in it. I looked at my watch. It was four minutes to one. Remember that. Four minutes to one, precisely.

I'd just walked the bridge from port to starboard when I heard a sound behind me, turned, and saw the bosun climbing the companion ladder. Then he spoke my name. I said: "Hot, isn't it? Can't you sleep below?"

"Beggin' your pardon, sir, but nobody's yet found me sleeping at my post!" The quartermaster was distinctly put out, and looked across at me as if I'd taken leave of my senses. I smiled. "Not you, quartermaster," I replied. "I wasn't talking to you but the bosun, here."

"Sorry, sir," he said, and looked across at the bosun and gave him one of those kind of half-pitying grins he always reserved for the older generation of sailors. The bosun ignored him and continued looking at me as if something was troubling him. Something was on his mind. His face was pale and strained in the bright moonlight. I said, "Anything you want?" but he turned and went down that ladder without a word.

192

At eight bells the first officer came on watch and we chatted awhile before I went below to my cabin and fell asleep instantly. My steward called me with a cup of coffee at one bell, in time for me to take the normal azimuth observation before breakfast. I shaved, washed, dressed, went up to the bridge and gave the first officer as cheerful a good morning as he had any right to expect. He was never what anybody might call a cheerful character, and this morning he looked like a man with the worries of the world on his shoulders. He said, "We'll be heaving to around sundown. The captain doesn't want to distress the passengers unduly. . . ."

Maybe I looked blank; I just stared, puzzled by his words.

"Yes. The usual thing. Burial services at sea are depressing ceremonies."

Then it dawned on me and I said, "The bosun." I wasn't asking the first officer a question; I was telling him, and he looked shocked.

"I was called to him shortly after I relieved you and found him in a bad state. It was obvious to me he was either dead or dying, so I summoned the doctor. And he said the bosun had died a few minutes before one o'clock."

"I could have told you that," I replied, "for he came up here on the bridge two or three minutes before one; I know, for I checked by the clock in the wheelhouse. He climbed the companion ladder and stood there without saying a word."

"You and he had a few things in common," he said.

I nodded. "We were square-rigger men. He came up here to say good-by."

I turned away. I found it difficult to say anything more and went to my cabin. The ship seemed somehow to have lost its soul. You know what I mean?

The first officer checked with the quartermaster and confirmed that he, too, had seen the bosun. Otherwise, I'd say, he had begun thinking I was getting senile and had imagined it all.

My host roused himself in the armchair and offered me a nightcap, but I thanked him and said no.

He was gone next morning when his wife brought coffee to my room; climbed into that skin-diving rig of his, she explained, and was out in the bay. As I stepped aboard the speedboat to return to the mainland I saw him surface and wave to me; then, as gracefully as a porpoise, he flipped over on his back and dived deep. A patch of bubbles was my last sight of him.

One day soon, I hope, I shall stop by at his house on the edge of that lapis lazuli bay; if I do, maybe we shall talk of French Pete again, and the bosun. . . .

15.

Shadows and Substance

ONE would like to think that there were always rational explanations for mysterious happenings at sea, if one probes deeply enough; but again and again reason fails us. I am like Professor Hecht, the German psychologist who investigated the matter of the haunted U-boat and reported: "This phenomenon does not lend itself to *any* explanation, and I can put forward no alternative theory to a supernatural agency." In the case of most of the incidents in this book, neither could I.

Conrad wrote of deep mysteries of the oceans, and his material gave the world fascinating stories of ships and men; but what might Conrad have done with the incident of the late fall of 1948, when ships within a hundred-mile area picked up an SOS from an unknown vessel, which gave no name and only her location, near the Malacca Straits? Two freighters arrived together and found the stricken ship drifting in calm seas, every member of the crew dead. They were sprawled around the deck, faces upturned, mouths gaping. There were no signs of violence. A fire was smoldering in one hold, and within thirty minutes a series of minor explosions occurred and the vessel went down. Nobody ever gave a satisfactory answer to this grim mystery.

But so far as "phantom" ships are concerned, maybe I can offer something in the nature of feasible explanation.

Take the case, for example, of the 5,438-ton freighter *Winding Gulf*, bound from European ports for Boston in the early winter of 1948. Nearing her destination, she encountered heavy fog, and then collided with some obstruction which damaged her badly. She managed to limp into port, where surveyors claimed that the damage had been caused by "a vessel obviously lying low in the water and laden with bulk freight."

No such vessel had been reported along the North Atlantic winter trade tracks and no other ship was in the vicinity of the *Winding Gulf* at that time. What had happened? Somebody suggested the "hoodoo" ship of the North Atlantic, the freighter *Dunmore*.

The *Dunmore* had been abandoned in mid-Atlantic by her master and crew; she was outward bound from Cardiff with bulk freight for Newfoundland, and, severely damaged in a storm, it looked as if she could remain afloat only a matter of hours. But, three months later, she caused minor damage to the 20-knot liner *St. Louis*; she was immediately regarded as a threat to all ships and a couple of units of the International Ice Patrol were ordered to seek her out, take her in tow or destroy her. They made contact, managed to put towlines aboard, but those lines were unshipped from the *Dunmore*'s deserted decks.

During the next four months three passenger vessels and a couple of warships sighted her in the Atlantic, heading south; two months later she was seen off the Grand Banks. In 1947, the United States Army transports *Joseph V. Connolly* and *General R. E. Callan* reported sighting on their radar an "unknown vessel lying low in the water laden with what seemed to be heavy freight." Exactly one year later there was the instance of *Winding Gulf* being damaged by an unknown vessel. The *Dunmore* was, in fact, not seen again after being sighted by the three passenger ships and two warships, and she may well have foundered almost immediately after; but she had earned herself the name of "hoodoo"—a ship that would never sink; and rumor among seamen has a habit of going the rounds pretty quickly.

A somewhat similar case was that of the schooner *Star* which, with a crew of thirteen, sailed out from Midway Island, struck a submerged coral reef and was abandoned. Her crew were picked up by the Glasgow bark *Ecclefechan* and landed none the worse for their experience. But their abandoned ship would have none of it; seven months later she sailed past Puget Sound; ninety days later she was sighted some four hundred miles due west of the Golden Gate; a Lloyds' agent on Fanning Island "spoke" with her by signal hoist and reported she seemed to be making good, going

3,500 miles from the original scene of her disaster. Four months slipped by, then she reached Hull Island, in the Phoenix group, and then disappeared forever.

Few folk these days can recall the mystery of the *Governor Parr*, abandoned in the fall of 1923, yet sighted on a number of subsequent occasions within twelve months. Four or five ships attempted to take her in tow, but somehow she always managed to break adrift; then she caught fire and was left to burn out and sink. The flames quenched themselves, however, and the *Governor Parr* was seen a month later, riding on an even keel. Obviously, she went down but nobody knows when or where.

There was, too, the case of the German freighter *Trave;* she was rammed outside San Francisco by a heavier vessel outward bound for Sydney, Australia, and sheared clean in two. Both parts started on independent voyages. Her stern eventually went ashore on the coast of New Guinea and was salvaged. The bow, which appeared to have suffered only minor damage, sailed on. An Australian passenger ship intercepted the forepart and attempted a tow, but the wreck slipped the cables, sailed away and finally made the Carolines, where it was driven ashore in bad weather and written off as scrap.

Similar instances of abandoned ships remaining afloat, derelict, could perhaps account for stories connected with the *Flying Dutchman*, the *Livera Nos*, and other legendary "ghost" ships, and here may be the rational explanation I was required to state. But there are many other incidents for which no such explanation can be offered; no alternative theory put forward to the supernatural.

Some months ago I visited an operational flying base and met a signal officer who served there throughout World War II. The story he told might well be fiction but, checking it, I accept it without question as fact.

It happened at this naval air base in the fall of 1942, at a time when morale was at pretty low ebb; Hitler was rampaging across Europe and seemed to be winning. There had been reverses everywhere and, at sea, supply ships were being torpedoed at an alarming rate. Hitler's air force, too, was battering opposition night and day.

That was bad enough, but there was another reason why morale was so low at this naval base. Pilots, fresh from preliminary flying courses in the United States and Canada, were being posted to the base for advanced training in handling operational aircraft from carriers. The only machines then available were British Spitfires and Hurricanes which had been in the Battle of Britain and were long past their prime. They had been converted hurriedly but were a lot the worse for wear. Consequently, accidents, many of them fatal, occurred with distressing frequency. Men were on edge; even the staff instructors showed signs of becoming jittery.

The signal officer takes up the story at this point:

We had been told that new kites were due any time, and God knows we had waited long enough for them.

Meantime, of course, training must continue with the emphasis on night operational duties, taking off and landing on carriers without assistance. Just normal blind-flying stuff, and that can be ticklish business even with modern aircraft. Our base commander was a man who rated discipline first, with personal feeling secondary. He knew that the boys were getting strained nerves but ignored it.

Five of the old crates were made ready and crews briefed for normal exercise one night; nobody spoke much and it was pretty clear they would be mighty glad when it was all over. They took off, made a circuit of the training base and things seemed to be okay . . . and then, clear and loud over the radio-telephone a voice called: "Hit the deck, you fools, fast! You'll die if you don't!"

Everybody heard it. The crews got it over their R/T clear as a bell, so did the men in our control tower; everybody. It scared the pants off us. Then we asked each other what would happen when the base commander heard. We didn't have to wait long. He stormed into the control tower and just as he did the voice came on the air a second time, then again. Those five kites pancaked quicker than anybody had ever seen it done and their crews spilled out fast. Their nerves had been shot to pieces.

Night flying was canceled, not that any of the boys would have taken an aircraft up after that—not until the new stuff arrived. Then, slowly, things got back to near normal. Every radio-telephone station within a hundred miles was checked—Army, Navy and Air Force—but nobody had been on the air that night. Some of the boys said the voice sounded like that of a pilot killed in a crash the previous day, but we were all tensed up and a man's imagination plays strange tricks at such times. Nobody ever discovered the origin of that voice and nobody ever will.

I made it my business to seek out and talk with pilots and ground crews who were on duty that night, checked and cross-checked their stories. They are middle-aged men now, but the passing years have done nothing to dim the memory of that night. *Or* that warning voice.

The schooner *Myone Kirby* was built around the turn of this century for slave-running between East African and Arabian ports and was employed in that terrible trade until she was sold on the open market, taken into dry dock, converted and rerigged from stem to stern and took shape as a passable seagoing yacht. She was part-owned by an ex-naval commander and a well-known actress.

Into Southampton she went in the early summer of 1937 for refit and stores preparatory to a long cruise around Middle Eastern ports. Her bosun, a dependable seaman, deserted, leaving a letter saying that as he lay sleeping in his bunk the previous night he was awakened by something unseen and then lifted from his bunk and pitched on the deck of his cabin. He was overcome with terror and fled on deck, but as he ran he felt two hands close around his throat, and he passed out. Nobody accepted the bosun's story. But when the owners threw a party the night before they sailed on their cruise, a woman guest who entered the saloon alone ran screaming for help, saying that fingers had closed around her neck and squeezed until she could hardly breathe. She managed to struggle free. She recovered, and said that when it happened she was conscious of a sickening smell.

The ex-commander tried laughing it off as "bilge-water we can never get rid of." But when I asked his honest opinion, he said: "Since the night the bosun went, there was something evil, hideously evil, about the ship."

Westward along the coast from the port of Southampton, on a shingle beach stretching away south-eastward into the Solent, and around one mile or so from the mainland, stands Hurst Castle, a magnificent old pile originally built as a fortress by Henry VIII between 1542 and 1544. To construct it, King Hal diverted much of the money and material he derived from his dissolution of the monasteries, and, indeed, much of the stonework came from old Beaulieu Abbey, in the New Forest.

Hurst remained a fortress through the years to the nineteenth century. It was occupied by British troops against Napoleon's threatened invasion of England, largely rebuilt around 1873 and scheduled as an ancient monument; it was taken over again by the British Army in September, 1939, and refortified against invasion by

Hitler's forces. (Though it has nothing to do with the incident, Charles I was held prisoner in the castle from November 30 to December 16, 1648, before he was taken to London and beheaded.)

One July afternoon, in 1957, three local youngsters, Roy Jenvey, Ben Ham and Colin Hillman, all about sixteen years of age and keen anglers, took out a dinghy and went fishing. Time means little to boys on such occasions. Before they knew it night had come down. They decided to return home, but cross-currents around that section of the coast had carried them off their course and made it tough going. It rained heavily but eventually the boys beached the dinghy and sheltered awhile in a disused boathouse; by now it was close on midnight and the weather had worsened.

Jenvey opened the boathouse door toward one o'clock to take a look at conditions, then called to his companions: "There's a large rowboat coming in. . . ."

They speculated about it and who might be its occupants; they wondered whether this was yet another attempted escape by young hoodlums from a reformatory on the Isle of Wight. It had been tried before, and a night like this was ideal.

The three boys watched as the boat was pulled silently shoreward and beached; they watched, terrified, as five hooded men stepped ashore—five figures clad in the white habits of monks. . . . And those five figures filed away toward old Beaulieu Abbey. Jenvey, Ham and Hillman told their story and were cross-questioned; the shore was examined at dawn but showed no trace of a boat. The heavy rains had obliterated every mark, even that of the fishing dinghy; but nobody denied that the experience was strange, uncanny, and nobody could offer an explanation.

In the fall of 1946, while on leave, I was at a police court when evidence was given by the fifteen-man crew of a small coastwise freighter, the *Hazelbank*, who had been charged with failing to carry out their captain's orders. The reason? They could not take their ship out, they claimed, because she was haunted by the ghost of a dead comrade killed some weeks before in a gale at sea. The men were discharged, but never went back aboard the *Hazelbank;* they said they would sooner starve than serve again in her.

In September, 1934, the brigantine *Lady of Avenel* made port after an uneventful voyage and her steward immediately deserted. He was found, arrested and charged; in the police court he explained that as he slept a woman's voice awakened him, crying for help. He went on deck but found no one; he got nervous and quit the ship. Nobody was prepared to accept his story until the ship's owner explained that while in port at the end of her previous voyage the vessel had been left in the care of a night watchman while her crew went ashore. During the night, eating a meal by the galley stove, the watchman had seen his oil lamp flicker and die out, although the watchman declared he had trimmed and filled it when he took over.

He relighted the lamp, and saw a woman appear through a nearby bulkhead, step toward him, turn away and disappear on deck. No woman had ever been aboard the brigantine.

Working on short-haul trade around the United Kingdom coastline is the sloop *Zebrina*, owned by a Bristol shipper. A trim, three-masted craft of 185-ton register, she was built at Whitstable, Kent, back in 1873 and worked the coast until, in World War I, she was taken over by the Navy and employed on patrol service in the English Channel under her master, I. A. Martin, and the normal crew of four men.

She served in this wartime capacity without incident until October, 1917, when she failed to return to her base. She was later discovered off Rozel Point, near Dielette, France, with all sails set and a meal laid in her crew quarters; her log, entered to three days previously, was in Martin's cabin. But neither he nor his crew were ever seen again. It was assumed that they had been taken prisoner aboard a U-boat and sent to Germany; but at the end of World War I investigations by the International Red Cross proved that this was not so. The fall of 1917 was not notable for bad weather conditions in the English Channel, so the idea that captain and crew had been washed overboard was ruled out. What became of them? Nobody has ever discovered their fate, and the manner of their disappearance, remains to this day as mysterious as that of the crew of the notorious *Mary Celeste*.

Wherever I have gone in search of material for this book, around Scandinavia, along the North German coast, from Holland down to Gibraltar, across the

North Atlantic, there have been stories in plenty. New England has a wealth of them, maybe the most outstanding that of a phantom Spanish ship, the *Sagunto*, lost with all hands around the year 1750. Oakum Bay, near Marblehead, has its own ghost, "The Shrieking Woman," said to have been slain by pirates in the mid-seventeenth century. Whittier wrote of the apparition:

> 'Tis said that often when the moon, is struggling
> With a gloomy even, and over moon and star is drawn
> The curtain of a clouded heaven,
> Strange sounds come up the narrow glen
> As if that robber crew was there;
> The hellish laugh, the shouts of men
> And a woman's dying prayer.

Sable Island had its specters, one especially known as the "Lady of Copeland," the ghost of a woman murdered by a smuggling gang. And Maine fishermen used to tell the story of the ship *Hascall*, which broke adrift from her moorings in heavy weather on George's Banks, collided with and sank the *Andrew Jackson* with all aboard. For generations after it was claimed that the ghosts of the drowned men came at midnight on the anniversary of the tragedy; and then no Gloucester man would dare take his boat out.

Fables? Who knows?

Some months before the Allied invasion of France, when large-scale training practice took place most days along the length of the English Channel, by error of judgment a flotilla of motor torpedo boats escorting landing craft with assault troops was attacked off the coast of Dorset by Allied fighter-bombers and destroyed with heavy loss of life. Some weeks later a similar tragedy took place along the coast westward.

During October, 1959, two British warships with other vessels raced to assist an unknown ship reported in distress off the Dorset-Devon coastline, in mid-Channel. She was said to be flying the flag of World War II's Free French forces and was reported as a 500-ton landing craft. The hours slipped past, then first reports arrived. The landing craft had been sighted, but it was deserted, with no sign of life aboard; nor had there been any response to Aldis lamp and radio signals. Some time later the skipper of the 1,875-ton Norwegian freighter *Rondo* reported locating the mystery ship and intended standing by until daylight. He signaled to the mainland: "She appears to be seaworthy," but added later, "From our present position now she seems to be getting under way and we may lose her before dawn."

The British minesweeper *Acute*, the frigate *Torquay* and the ocean-going salvage tug *Turmoil*, which played a leading part in the loss of *Flying Enterprise* in 1952, together with two Dutch ships and a German freighter, crammed on speed and went to assist the *Rondo*. But neither those ships, nor anybody ashore or afloat, ever sighted that mysterious landing craft again. She just disappeared into thin air.

Known to many transatlantic voyagers some years ago was the Italian liner *Utopia;* outward bound she was in collision with the British warship *Anson*, damaged and sunk. Salvaged, dry-docked, she was refitted and then returned to her normal run. But she made only one voyage and was then withdrawn and sold as scrap. The reason was that her officers, crew and a number of passengers claimed that they heard "the voices of the dead" as the *Utopia* steamed past the scene of her sinking.

Mere superstition? Maybe. The legendary misfortunes which befell seamen in Coleridge's *Ancient Mariner* were visited on thirty men among the crew of the 15,000-ton freighter *Calpean Star*, in the summer of 1959. The vessel reached Liverpool at the end of a five-month round-trip voyage to South Georgia; her freight consisted of 5,000 tons of whale-meat products. Off Bird Island, South Georgia, an albatross, that legendary bird of ill omen to all seafaring men, was shot down by an amateur archer with a home-made bow and arrow, but not killed. It was cared for throughout the return passage to the British port and arrived there strong and well. It was valued at around five hundred dollars, offered by a German zoo.

In Liverpool, for no known reason, the albatross died, and thirty members of the crew walked off the ship, refusing to serve aboard another hour. They were paid off, and the remainder of the men at once staged a sit-down strike. An officer of the ship said to me: "This seems to be an apt climax; ever since the day that bird was shot all manner of inexplicable things have gone wrong, but none of us wants to talk about them. They were just a strange string of even stranger incidents. It was as if a hoodoo descended on the ship and every man aboard."

Can there be a rational explanation for such a matter as this? These are not the days of the *Ancient Mariner*, but of rockets around the moon; and I submit that nobody can ever confidently assure the average seaman that age-old superstition of the seas is as dead as the proverbial dodo.

Toward the end of my search for material which I could include in this book I met an artist, a level-headed woman living in Northern Ireland. Her hobby, and a highly profitable one at that, was designing jewelry. She told me she had once had what she called "an unpleasant experience" aboard a cruise liner in the summer of 1938, on a voyage around Africa. She confessed, "It is the only time in my life I've been really scared," and, for a while, she was not prepared to go beyond that brief statement. Eventually, I managed to draw the story out and I offer it, as she did, in good faith.

The cruise ship was *Llanstephan Castle*, 11,346 tons, owned by the Union-Castle Line of London. Built in 1914 at Govan, she was designed to carry 229 first-class and 202 tourist-class passengers. During World War I the liner served as a troop ship and from 1919 to 1939 was on the London-East Africa service. Set down in her own words, here is the uncanny experience of this cruise passenger:

For some months I had wanted to make a long cruise and see something of places I had never visited before, so I booked a cabin in the *Llanstephan Castle*, intending to exchange the wet, cold and long winter of Ireland for some weeks of sunshine. The advent of the Munich crisis for a while made it problematical whether the cruise would in fact take place, but as events proved, the international crisis was settled temporarily and I reached London to do some shopping before going aboard.

We embarked at Tilbury on a damp and dismal day. About three days out we encountered bad weather and the ship was badly battered by heavy seas, a considerable amount of damage being done to her fittings, and three members of the crew were injured. An officer told me he had never known conditions like this in the many years he had been in the service; and at Gibraltar the weather continued so rough it was impossible for any passengers to go ashore. A Naval hospital tender came alongside us and removed the injured seamen. That evening, my steward told me that the liner had for some two years been considered unlucky and that strange things were continually happening aboard, but I dismissed the story as imagination on the part of a rather badly rattled man. But he was quite serious; he said there had been a suicide aboard in the course of the last three voyages, and accidents which ought never to have happened. Then he said: "Maybe I should not have mentioned these things. I'm sorry."

I dismissed it from mind, for there was quite a lot to prepare for, the ship being scheduled to call at Tangier and then Genoa. I dined at the chief officer's table together with six other passengers but we never seemed able to really get together; nor for that matter did any other passengers and it was as if an air of oppression surrounded us all. I could not define it, but it was apparent. We sailed from Genoa for Port Said where

I went ashore with one or two other folk and made the usual round of sight-seeing tours.

We sailed through the Suez Canal and finally reached Beira; but still that strange, heavy atmosphere prevailed. It wasn't the heat, which was oppressive, but something that seemed to wrap itself around the ship and all aboard. On the way south to Durban, in perfectly calm seas, the ship suddenly developed an alarming list and it was suggested that the cargo had shifted. I asked the chief officer whether any danger existed, but he laughed and replied that the chief steward was to blame for broaching and emptying the fresh-water storage tanks on one side of the ship without any thought for trimming the vessel. It seemed a strange explanation to me, but I could not dispute it.

When we reached Durban, however, I was told that a member of the ship's catering department had disappeared and it was thought had deserted the ship. It was after leaving Durban that I went out on deck around eleven o'clock at night, being unable to sleep and thinking that a walk around the upper promenade deck might make me want to go to bed. Nobody else was in sight and all I could see was the dim light burning over the main entrance to the saloon. I stopped walking and looked up at the sky; it was a lovely night. And then something indistinct approached me; it moved slowly and with what seemed to be a cold purpose. And as it came nearer I saw that it was the figure of a man in uniform, and that the clothing was dripping with some strange greenish slime. I knew then, why I cannot say, that it intended taking hold of me and pushing me over the ship's rail, and I was so terrified I was unable to move or to call for help. The thought seemed to come to my mind—what would my family think? For I had no reason to commit suicide. I tried to move. I prayed. There is no shame in admitting that. I prayed as I had never done before.

Then I found I was able to move, and I ran as fast as I could toward the bow of the ship and finally reached my cabin in a roundabout manner. There was a window, not just a round porthole, over my bed and it was open about six inches. I flung myself at it and tried to close it, but something on deck outside prevented my doing so. How long I stood there I cannot say, but in time I reopened my cabin door and ran across to a nearby bathroom; somehow I thought I would be safer locked in there. And as I locked the door I knew that this thing in tattered uniform was with me. I managed to unlock the door and fled back to my cabin. The window was still open, and I watched the fingers of a hand take hold of the upper sash. I ran from the cabin again and managed to reach the cabin of a woman friend and there I spent the rest of the terrifying night. I was far too frightened by the experience to talk about it to anybody, and we reached Teneriffe. Two days later the ship's doctor was on deck at around 10 P.M. and discovered a woman passenger poised on the ship's rail, dressed in a negligee, about to leap overboard. He dragged her to safety and kept her in his care until the ship returned to Southampton; but I am certain that the ship's doctor did not see that unspeakable thing which had failed to kill me and was trying to kill this second woman.

That is the story, and who am I to doubt it? The liner was refitted in Belfast after World War II, went back to the round-Africa service and was sold for breaking up in March, 1952. So, presumably, her hoodoo died with her. Who knows?

Around the turn of this century, quarter-deck officers in the British Fleet had a contemptuous term for colleagues who forsook the spit-and-polish of a warship for the grime and dungarees of submarine life. They called it "the Trade." Nobody at that time knew that men who volunteered to serve in "the Trade" established a brotherhood honored throughout naval service everywhere; men who went out to pit their skill and courage against hazards quite unimaginable; men prepared to dice with death in times of war—*and of peace*. Men whose active life was spent inside a throbbing steel shell crammed with a nightmare pattern of machinery with around half an inch of metal between them and a monstrous pressure of thousands of tons of water outside.

I am lucky enough to count among my best friends a number of submariners and on a few occasions have been privileged to share a voyage with them. There is no sign of flurry or fluster as sailing hour draws near; each man is at his appointed post looking a trifle bored, with that vacant look you see on the face of a long-distance bus or truck driver waiting to pull out with a load. But, unlike a long-distance bus, or the cab of a big truck, submarines offer little elbow space, for their designers always appeared to begrudge space to human beings. . . .

The more sober-minded of British newspapers, on the morning of Wednesday, April 18, 1951, carried headlines which announced that contact had been made after day-and-night search with the submarine *Affray* and that she had been finally located, with all available rescue ships converging on the spot where she was said to be. The press, with banner headlines, merely announced: "*Affray* Found!" And the hearts of millions of ordinary folk were raised with hope; though the sub-headline, "Crew alive on sea bed," brought many a cold shudder to everybody who heard the grim news.

The *Affray* was laid down January 16, 1944, and launched April 12, 1945; she was completed May 2, 1946. Of Britain's "A" class, she measured 1,500 tons displacement.

Early in April, 1951, she received orders; she had been selected to carry out a short training course and was to embark twenty junior naval officers, an instructor, four royal marines, together with her normal complement—a total of seventy-five men.

She sailed from the naval base, Portsmouth, late in the day, April 16, to steer a course south of the Isle of Wight and dive at 9:16 P.M., making a steady 4½ knots for Falmouth where she was scheduled to surface between eight and eight-thirty the next morning. Her commander had orders to report time of diving, speed during the short voyage down-Channel, routine conditions and behavior aboard. In the event of mishap, or distress, the *Affray* could do one, or all, of five things: Shoot up red and yellow marker buoys which light at night; fire smoke signals from two of her compartments; transmit radio signals if not deeper than periscope depth; use supersonic sound telegraphy if on the sea bed, though only other ships equipped with supersonic gear, not shore stations, could pick up such messages; or pump oil to the surface as a guide to searching ships and aircraft.

On the night of April 16 the *Affray* signaled: "Am diving," and then proceeded on her course westward. She then remained silent that Monday evening, but the subsequent alarm received no publicity until Wednesday; the following Admiralty official statements take up the story:

1. The submarine *Affray* has not surfaced as expected after diving while on exercises. She sailed from Portsmouth unescorted and dived at 2115 south of the Isle of Wight. She was proceeding westward submerged at a speed of 4½ knots.

2. She was expected to surface at 0830 this morning but no surfacing signal has been received and her present position is unknown. Naval craft including helicopters have been alerted and begun search and five destroyers have put to sea. Every attempt is being made to contact the submarine by radio.

3. The following message is being broadcast hourly to shipping: "Submarine missing, possibly sunk between positions 50° 10′ N., 1° 45′ W., 49° 40′ N., 4° W. Vessels in the vicinity are requested to keep sharp lookout for survivors and to report wreckage, oil slicks on the surface or any other indications to the Commander in Chief, Portsmouth."

4. Vessels engaged in the search include six submarines, two United States destroyers, six frigates, six destroyers, various aircraft and helicopters.

5. The weather forecast is quite good. It is neap tides, which means that the rise and fall of the tide is the minimum.

6. The *Affray* was carrying out a war patrol and was due to make Falmouth; this means that on passage she would have been continually submerged and at times at considerable depth. In her orders she was, however, required to report herself hourly. No such report has been received. She may be proceeding submerged, having misread her orders for these regular reports. If in so doing she is carrying out a deep diving patrol she would not be able to pick up messages which are being made to her every fifteen minutes by Rugby radio station.

7. In view of the lapse of time the chances of the submarine having misinterpreted her instructions are lessening and the chances of an accident must be regarded as increasingly probable.

The submarine had sufficient oxygen for three days and, assuming that she was undamaged and there was no flooding, enough Davis escape equipment on board for every member of her crew and her specially embarked officer training complement; she had an escape hatch in the gun tower and three twill trunks in various parts of her hull which, lowered into position under hatches, formed escape chambers.

Then came reports that contact had been made with the *Affray;* that she was believed to be lying on an even keel, almost as if in dry dock, in 33 fathoms, around 200 feet, 10 miles due south of Bournemouth, on the Hampshire coast. The submarine *Sea Devil* reported receiving supersonic signals from the *Affray* and that, said the British Admiralty, showed that "at least some of the seventy-five men on board are alive." Then a naval diver from the salvage ship H.M.S. *Reclaim*, working in an observation chamber 260 feet down, reported that he had directed the light from his powerful arc lamp on an object and had made out the letters F F R A Y; the first letter of the name was not clear. But, and mark this fact clearly, this last report came *fifty-nine days after* the *Affray* sailed from Portsmouth Naval Base; and now the Admiralty reserved judgment on all theories that were put forward; in fact, it was officially said, "It may be weeks before the full story is known." It never was known; not to the complete satisfaction of everybody concerned.

In actual fact, the *Affray* traveled, safely submerged, something like eight hours from the moment she signaled "Am diving," a distance of nearly forty miles; and that placed her, when she was finally traced, to a point less than a dozen miles due north of Alderney, Channel Islands; she was found at a depth never explored by man. There were no survivors, and there she lies to this day. . . .

On the night the submarine sailed from Portsmouth and at approximately thirty minutes after she signaled "Am diving," the wife of a British rear admiral was about to retire to bed for the night at her home in Guernsey, Channel Islands. She told me this fantastic story, which I accept without any qualification:

> Quite suddenly, I realized I was not alone in my room and in the half light I recognized my visitor. He had been serving as an engineer officer in my husband's ship, a cruiser, at a time when my husband was en-

gineer-commander, and we had often entertained him in our Channel Islands home.

He approached me and then stood still and silent; I was astonished to see him dressed in normal submariner's uniform although I did not recognize this fact until later when I described his clothing to my husband. Then he spoke quite clearly, and said: "Tell your husband we are at the north end of Hurd Deep, nearly seventy miles from the lighthouse at St. Catherine's Point. It happened very suddenly and none of us expected it." After that the speaker vanished.

I immediately spoke to my husband by telephone, for he was then in a shore appointment in England, and to my dismay he told me, first, that he was not aware that this young officer was even in the *Affray*, nor that he had volunteered for the submarine service. It was all very puzzling. We spoke again by telephone to each other a few days later, when my husband told me that the search was being carried out in quite a different part of the Channel from where my visitor had indicated to me—and, as you know, wrongly, as it turned out later. This being so, my husband said, there did not seem to be anything he could do about it.

The *Affray* dived on the evening of April 16; she was finally located on June 14 by H.M.S. *Reclaim*, using underwater television cameras, 228°, around sixty-seven miles off St. Catherine's Lighthouse, thirty-seven miles southwest of her reported diving position; she lay in forty-three fathoms on the very edge of Hurd Deep.

Weeks later the submarine's Snort tube was recovered and brought ashore; examination showed no marks of damage which could have been caused by collision.

but it was fractured two to three feet from its base and was found lying on the port side at right angles to the hull. The cause of the fracture was later said to be due to fault in design and material. Investigations showed that all hatches of the submarine were shut tight, indicator buoys were housed and hydroplanes set to surface the ship.

Quite recently, I spoke of this tragedy with a group of naval officers and one of them said: "If you had been the husband of that woman, what would you have done? Remember, she was visited by what we can only call the wraith of this young officer thirty minutes only after the ship dived and before any alarm was raised. So—what would you have done? Contacted the Admiralty and risk being laughed at? No; in my opinion, though it makes one wonder what might have been the result if the telephone call had been brought to the attention of the Admiralty, I imagine that the accident, whatever it was, must have been almost immediately fatal, or else that vision would never have occurred." A second officer said: "I've had this same type of vision in my own family, and when checked it was proved to be correct. Death or serious injury leading to loss of life was the cause; but the strange thing was that these visions were not made to the person most closely concerned with the victim but to some near and dear and trusted friend."

It was a harrowing experience for this woman, alone in her home and powerless to help, and she added: "I think it would be terribly painful to the boy's family, and to the families of every man aboard the submarine, to read your book. I do not want to tell you the name of the officer concerned, and it would be better were you not to mention either my own name or that of my husband, nor the name of his ship, if you can avoid it."

I respect her wish. Incidents such as this, and the others that I have recorded, are beyond my understanding and, with Professor Hecht, I can find no alternative theory to some supernatural agency. Much of what I have written, therefore, may seem complete nonsense to the average shore dweller. But to the average sea-faring man all things are possible.